The Individual in Society

The Individual in Society

Bob Hallawell
RNMH, RMN, CertEd, BA, MBA,
Quality Management Project Officer,
Mid-Trent College of Nursing
and Midwifery, Nottingham

and

Richard Brittle
RNMH, CertEd, Nurse Teacher,
Mid-Trent College of Nursing
and Midwifery, Nottingham

Scutari Press • London

A division of Scutari Projects Ltd., the publishing company of the Royal College of Nursing

First published 1995

British Library Cataloguing in Publication Data
Hallawell, Bob
  Individual in Society
  I. Title II. Brittle, Richard
  302.5
  ISBN 1–871364–99–X

Typeset by Greenshires Icon, Exeter
Printed and bound in Great Britain by
Redwood Books, Trowbridge, Wiltshire

Contents

Acknowledgements

Thanks to our respective partners Sandy and Rebecca for tolerance of our absence from all normal domestic activities during the writing of this text and for encouragement, support and constructive criticism. Thanks also to Paula Rhodes for assistance with Chapter 2; to Caroline for infinite patience in wordprocessing our scribbled efforts and understanding our requirements in an almost telepathic manner, and to Jim who got used to hearing, 'It will be finished next month, definitely.' Finally, we are grateful to those students and colleagues of the Mid-Trent College who assisted in the development of this text.

Introduction

This book has been developed to provide students of nursing and midwifery with a flexible, self-directed means of study. It offers a mode of study which will enable students to control the rate and depth of their own learning. The student is guided through written text and activities which enable achievement of specified learning objectives.

The learning activities are both described in written text and indicated by the use of symbols. The symbols used and their associated meanings are as follows:

Activity

You will be requested to undertake an activity, based on the text just read, or as an introduction to an issue.

Group Activity

At times certain activities may be enhanced by group participation and discussion.

Reflective Points

In completing the text activities, issues and implications will emerge. You are requested to 'think about' or reflect on these, and how they may relate to you personally or professionally.

Reading

At times you may be requested to read additional texts or may have texts recommended to you for further reading or interest.

You should also note that following each of the activities in this book are sections containing *our* responses to the activities. These responses are intended to act as guidelines, in order that you may better evaluate your own interactions with the book. You may well find that your responses differ from ours; this does not necessarily mean that either of us is 'right' or 'wrong'. Some activities require you to consider personal issues for which there may be no 'right' answers. Similarly, at times you may be drawing on your own knowledge, skills and individual experiences which will quite naturally differ from those of the authors. What is more important than potential differences between our responses is that you attempt each of the activities *before* looking at the guidelines. We feel that such an approach will greatly enhance your learning opportunities.

As you may have gathered from the title of the book, the focus is on individuals and their positions within society. In order to achieve this focus the book draws for the most part upon the social sciences of psychology and sociology. This is not, however, a distant academic activity; it involves you, the student, in examining yourself, both as a person and a professional, and your impact on others. The aim is to facilitate self-awareness as much as awareness of others in our society. Stockwell (1972) suggests this aim in arguing that the study of behavioural sciences should focus on understanding ourselves, and how we react to others, as much as on seeking to understand the patient.

To provide the food for thought which will stimulate raised awareness, the book draws on the application of the social sciences to potentially neglected areas of care. Many of the areas examined are contentious in nature and rich in learning material. Because of this, however, it is recognised that this book is no ABC or definitive guide to nursing and midwifery. It is not intended to be. You will each extract different points of interest, different views and different perspectives from the text. There will also be points at which knowledge and skill development will be shared.

We have built the book around five areas which we feel should be of concern to all nurses and midwives seeking to achieve maximum health gain for the recipients of their services. These five areas of concern are examined in turn within each of the chapters of the book.

Chapter 1 is entitled **Psychological and Sociological Dimensions** and introduces the student to the study of social sciences, particularly psychology and sociology. The chapter goes on to examine the role of the individual in society, societal, social and personal behaviour, and factors influencing such behaviours, laying the foundation for study of the subsequent chapters.

Chapter 2 addresses **Divisions in Society** and how these may have an impact on the role of the nurse or midwife. Divisions such as class, race and gender are examined from both a historical and a contemporary perspective and are related to the provision of health-care within our society. Inequalities in health are also given specific consideration.

Chapter 3 focuses on **Labelling Theory and Stigma**, considering how and why we use labels, and how stereotyping, prejudice and discrimination may develop and be manifest in identified behaviours. Particular reference is made to the experiences of people with a learning disability and people with a mental health disorder. Consideration is also given to the application of labels, and consequent behaviours within adult nursing environments.

Chapter 4 examines the role of institutions in our society and the effects that these may have on the individual. Hence the title **Institutions and Institutionalisation.** The role of institutions in society is then applied to health care settings with a focus on the role of hospitals and how institutional practices influence the lives of those people using the service.

Finally, Chapter 5 addresses a more personal issue for the student, that of **Communication and Caring.** We look at how people communicate and how to improve the effectiveness of message-communication. The principles of communication are related to the experiences of patients/clients throughout the chapter.

This brief overview may help you to target particular areas of interest. Each chapter has been designed as a self-contained unit of study, so that you can choose to interact with any one chapter on its own or study them all in sequence. Either approach will be of equal benefit. This also means that you can study the book over any length of time that you choose, coming back to it when necessary or when you have the time.

One other facility which has been provided at the back of the book is a set of **self-evaluation questions** for each of the chapters. These have been included in order that you may test your own learning once you have completed a given chapter.

No answers are given to the self-evaluation questions; you will need to return to the chapter text and search for the answers if necessary. We feel sure that you will get the most benefit from this book if you make use of the self-evaluation questions.

In this brief introduction we have tried to give you an outline of the contents, a guide to its use and some reasons for its relevance to your studies of nursing and midwifery. The book is both about awareness of others and of yourself and about how such awareness may achieve health gain for your future patients/clients. We wish you well in your endeavours and hope that you enjoy this book.

If only we knew what we were about perhaps we could go about it better.

ABRAHAM LINCOLN

Bob Hallawell
Richard Brittle

Note: Throughout this book the authors have avoided the use of 'him/her', 'he/she' etc. and have opted for the less clumsy 'them', 'they', 'their' etc., wherever possible.

Reference

Stockwell F (1972) *The Unpopular Patient.* London: Royal College of Nursing.

CHAPTER 1

Psychological and Sociological Dimensions

There is nothing as practical as a good theory

GEORGE KELLY

1 Psychological and Sociological Dimensions

Introduction

Our lives are strongly affected and determined by others; how others think about us and how we, in turn, think about ourselves often influences our behaviour. Specific social situations influence our behaviour as well, and this social behaviour is governed both by perceptions and social norms.

Our interactions with others may be brief or sporadic, long-lasting or continuous, and influence us in varying degrees. For the nurse or midwife, study of psychology and sociology is essential in order to understand the behaviour of people and their social situations.

Care professionals come into contact with people at all stages in the life cycle and the insights into human development offered by psychology and sociology can enhance effective practice. Holistic need/satisfaction for patients/clients is facilitated by knowledge of psychological, spiritual and social influences on health and well-being and of the links between these factors and physical health.

Nurses and midwives seek to deliver unique programmes of care which meet the unique needs of the individual. Understanding human uniqueness in turn enables them to identify human similarities; the possession of such information promotes optimum intervention strategies.

Starr and Goldstein (1975) offer the following principles of human relations:

- *In order to understand the meaning of an individual's behaviour we must know a great deal about her [him] and her [his] inner world*

- *Understanding behaviour requires that information be gathered to support the proposed hypothesis*

- *Multiple causation for behaviour is the norm*

- *Behaviour has multiple levels and people can function on many levels*

- *Behaviour analysis must take account of social context*

STARR AND GOLDSTEIN, 1975

To understand truly the diversity of personalities, the uniqueness of individuals, the distinction between overt behaviour and underlying dynamics and the social influences on behaviour, we can make the use of the concepts, principles, approaches and research findings of the fields of psychology and sociology.

Objectives

After working through this chapter you should be able to:

1 Understand the importance of **psychology** and **sociology** to, and their application within, effective care practices.

2 Outline the **main approaches** within psychology and sociology.

3 Identify and describe **society** and its main components.

4 Understand how **social order**, **social control** and **social change** may influence **individual behaviour**.

5 Explain the process of **socialisation**.

6 Discriminate between **compliance** and **conformity**.

7 Identify why people **obey authority**.

8 Describe how and why **social conflict** manifests itself.

9 Understand how individual **deviance** may benefit society, social change and the activities of nurses/midwives.

10 Describe the **componential** and **functional** approaches toward the explanation of **attitudes**.

11 Explain the role of **cognitive consistency theories** in understanding **attitude formation** and **change**.

12 Apply the knowledge gained to **effective practice** which optimises **health gain** for clients/patients.

Psychology and Sociology

The social sciences – that is, those disciplines which study human behaviour and societies – include sociology, psychology, economics, political science, anthropology and history. This chapter, and indeed the book itself, focuses primarily on the first two of these: psychology and sociology.

Law, public administration, social medicine, social work, education, business administration, nursing and midwifery are all professional arenas which use the social sciences to provide interventions for practical problems. The social sciences provide insights into human behaviour.

Why do people behave as they do?

There is not, of course, a simple answer to this question. People are complex and unpredictable. However, we can use the knowledge bases of psychology and sociology to develop understanding of individuals and their behaviour. It is widely recognised in contemporary nursing and midwifery arenas that a deeper understanding of human behaviour is not only beneficial and useful, but is also a necessity for the achievement of effective care practices which promote health gain.

We could approach the question of behaviour through the identification of individual similarities and differences.

List those factors which might make people different from one another

The factors set out in Table 1.1 are often put forward in response to this question.

Physical	Psychological	Social
Body shape/build	Personality	Clothing
Skin pigmentation	Temperament	Lifestyle
Height	Emotions	Homes
Weight	Confidence	Accent
Hair colour and	Intelligence	Language
distribution on the body	Motivation	Hobbies
Eye colour	Memory	Interests
Facial features	Thought processes	Wealth
Age	Perception	Income
Health	Values	Occupation
Fitness	Coping strategies	Religion
Metabolism	Beliefs	Behaviour
Coordination	Attitude	Culture
Agility	Knowledge	Class
Speed of movement	Empathy	Ethnicity
Use of special senses		

Table 1.1. Differences between people

You may have thought of other factors but even if you did not the list is indicative of human complexity.

 Given such complexity can we sensibly believe that standardised, routinised approaches to care will actually benefit patients/clients?

What is also important to recognise is that any one of the listed factors may impinge on health gain should it distort the individual's lifestyle. Health is not simply a physical state; it must be thought of holistically; recognition must be given to the totality of individual experiences and being.

Psychology

Psychology may be thought of as a science which focuses on the study of behaviour and mental processes (Atkinson *et al.*, 1990). Therefore psychology concentrates on the behaviour of individuals rather than on the wider societal sphere, and enables the nurse or midwife to view the person as consisting of a mind as well as a body, both of which require care interventions (McGhie, 1973).

To facilitate an understanding of self and others, psychology makes use of theories, hypotheses, research and observation. Theories are constructed from scientific observation of human behaviour and consist of general systems which are both logical and coherent. They propose patterns of behaviour which can be verified by independent observation and research. Once the theory is demonstrated to be both valid and reliable it can be used to explain existing behaviour and to predict future behaviour (Starr and Goldstein, 1975).

Nurses and midwives use theories, in much the same way as psychologists, in order to understand their patients/clients and to make predictions about their probable behaviour. Theories are also important for health professionals as they are the basis for consistency of professional behaviour and procedures. The assumption that nursing and midwifery are essentially 'commonsense' activities does a disservice to their theoretical underpinnings.

Increasingly, nursing and midwifery practices are sought to be research-based; practice is based on tested hypotheses, observation and verification.

A number of distinct perspectives exist within the field of psychology, as shown in Figure 1.1. Each of these perspectives offers a different explanation for individual action and each can promote perception of the total person. There are a number of prominent people associated with each perspective including:

Behavioural	– Watson, Pavlov, Skinner, Thorndike, Hull, Tolman
Psychoanalytic	– Freud, Jung, Adler, Horney, Sullivan, Fromm, Erikson

Phenomenological – Maslow, Rogers, Kelly, Berne

Cognitive – Ebbinghaus, Bartlett, Tulving, Piaget

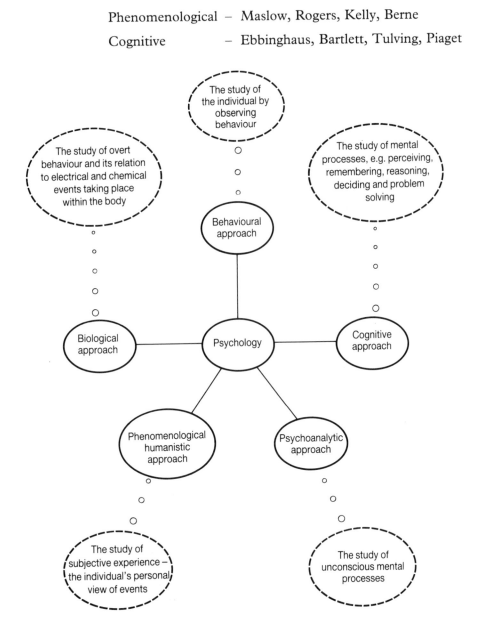

Figure 1.1. Psychological perspectives

However, the individual focus of psychology might on its own be too constrictive. Considering people outside their social context may lead to a distorted perception of their behaviour. Social psychology attempts to address this problem by focusing study on social behaviour and thought processes. Use of social psychology facilitates understanding and prediction of human behaviour within the context of complex, diverse social situations (Pennington, 1986).

Why seek to understand and predict behaviour? Well, because without prediction and understanding an organised society would soon disintegrate and collapse. The study of psychology helps us to understand individuals and their behaviour. In order to understand the significance and impact of that behaviour in social situations consideration must also be given to sociology.

Sociology

Sociology is concerned with the interactions that people have with each other. The many facets of social living such as social interaction, cooperation and conflict, and individuals and their social relationships are essential study areas for sociologists (Congalton, 1976).

Therefore the area of study widens to look beyond the individual; to observe and proffer explanations for their social relationships. This observing of relationships among others enables us as individuals to develop personal identities and exercise autonomy in our lifestyles.

> *Sociology deals with the analysis of patterned social relationships in modern societies. Parodoxically, becoming aware of how social relationships shape our lives may make us freer to be who we want to be.*

PERSELL, 1990

Sociology enables us to examine how social structures such as institutions, for example the family, religion and education (*see* Chapter 4), as well as social inequalities (*see* Chapter 2) and stigma/prejudice (*see* Chapter 3) influence personal identities.

The division and study of the social world at discrete levels is possible, Persell (1990) identifies four such levels: micro, organisational, institutional and macro.

- The **micro level** relates to how the individual feels and thinks about their social world, how it has a subjective effect upon them and their interactions with others. The micro level is concerned with the meanings people attach to social actions.

- The **organisational level** enables the study of formal organisations and the social life of the larger societal groups.

- The **institutional level** examines how patterned activities facilitate the satisfaction of important social needs. Needs such as obtaining food or raising children are often facilitated in societal institutions the study of which develops knowledge regarding interinstitutional relationships and institutional variances between societies.

- The **macro level** makes a comparison across whole societies or compares changes in entire societies over time.

The early sociologists included August Comte (1798–1857), Herbert Spencer (1820–1903), Karl Marx (1818–1883), Emile Durkheim (1858–1917), George Simmel (1858–1918) and Max Weber (1864–1920).

THE INDIVIDUAL IN SOCIETY

It is not possible to examine the work of each of these individuals separately in this text. However, interested readers might like to peruse:

Persell C H (1990) *Understanding Society – An Introduction to Sociology*, 3rd Edition, pp. 10–14. London: Harper & Row.

The modern sociologists include Talcott Parsons (1902–1979), Robert K Merton, Lewis Coser, Barry Wellman, S D Berkowitz, Peter Blau, George Herbert Mead, Charles Horton Cooley, Erving Goffman and Harold Garfinkel. The work of these individuals has been encapsulated within five major approaches to sociology which are outlined in Table 1.2.

Persell gives a more detailed explanation of the approaches on pp. 15–20 of her book.

An approach not yet mentioned but which may be of particular interest to nurses and midwives is that of sociobiology. This approach centres on the biological basis for human behaviour and looks to biological theory to explain social activity (Persell, 1990).

Sociobiology provides a forum for discussion of the 'nature *vs* nurture' argument – that is, whether behaviour is biologically determined or shaped by culture. A widely accepted view is that while their biology provides humans

	Marxist	Weberian	Functionalist	Network	Interpretative
Who?	Marx	Weber Collins Coser Lenski	Comte Durkheim Parsons Merton	Wellman Berkowitz Blau (exchange theory)	Mead Cooley Goffman (symbolic interaction), Garfinkel (ethnomethodology)
Focus	change process	change process	stability	change or stability	change or stability
Interrelation	objective	objective or subjective	objective	objective or subjective	subjective
Level of study	organisational, institutional or macro	organisational, institutional, macro or micro	organisational, institutional or macro	organisational, institutional, macro and micro	micro and organisational

Table 1.2. The major approaches to sociology

with a wide range of potentialities, environment and culture are the keys to behavioural variations within this range.

An outline has been given of the theoretical approaches and areas of study of sociology. How do you think sociology relates to nursing, midwifery and health studies?

The activities of nurses and midwives do not take place in isolation from their social context. That is, they take place within a wider society and involve interaction with others. Sociology can provide nurses and midwives with new perspectives or deeper knowledge of social events and human behaviour.

Similarly, both health and illness cannot be considered to be solely physical entities. The concept of mental health acknowledges influences other than the physical, and conditions such as 'disability' are argued by some to be a 'social creation'. That is, disability is both defined and constrained by society; if you doubt this, check with a disabled person their individual perception of their health status and compare it with that generally held by society at large. These are usually different.

Societal factors such as poverty, unemployment, prejudice, discrimination, homelessness, class differences, racism, sexism and inadequate social networks all influence health gain or loss. (Some of these areas will be addressed in greater detail later in this book.) In order to understand the totality of the patient's/client's experience, the nurse/midwife must look beyond the immediate care environment to the wider social arena, from the organisational level to the macro level.

Consider also the following specific issues:

- Social change which leads to increased expectation of, and consequent demands upon, health service provision;

- Changes in demand for services prompted by demographic fluctuations;

- The changing social structures and processes of the National Health Service;

- Social change in the provision of education and training for nurses and midwives;

- Political and economic influences on health care provision;

- Social factors impinging on health gain and loss;

- Inequalities in society underlying inequalities in health;

- Meeting health needs in a multiracial/cultural society.

There should be no doubt in your mind that studying psychology and sociology is as pertinent to effective intervention as are biological science and nursing/midwifery theory and practice.

We now move on to the macro level of sociological analysis and focus on **societies**.

Societies

Without an established society it is unlikely that individuals could survive and without doubt their development as people would be radically different.

 Note your definition of a society.

A society can be defined in terms of culture, territory, unity and differentiation. People within a given society share a distinct culture which is enacted within a defined territory. Thus they feel some unity as a group, a national identity, which sets them apart from other people and societies. A sense of unity is also promoted by the existence of structured relationships between people and the presence of recognisable patterns of activity which are rooted in historical development.

It can be seen that societies develop over time and structures emerge which coordinate individual action. The ability of individuals to act independently, the notion of individual agency, has to be considered in the light of broader societal influences. Societal change is promoted by broad influences such as modifications in the relationships between societal groups. Society must thus be considered at group rather than individual level in order to be truly understood (Open University, 1986).

 Do societies have characteristics in common or share processes?

All societies have a culture together with identifiable social structures. In addition stratification of some form, such as social class, is found in all societies. Finally, the family as a foundation for social organisation is always present although the particular forms of manifestation may differ (Congalton, 1976).

List those structures that you recognise to be inherent parts of society.

Societies have structure; that is one can identify patterned relationships within society which can be conglomerated under the heading of social structure. Social structure includes:

- **Social institutions** – successful patterned responses to the demands of society (described further in Chapter 4).

- **The division of labour** – meaning the assignment of specialised tasks to specific members of a group, organisation, community or society. Thus nurses specialise in nursing and gas-fitters do not.

- **Social ranking** – inequality in the control of resources leads to differentiation in rank – unequal positions in society.

- **Social status** – each individual has a socially defined position in society which affords them both rights and responsibilities. Status may be either ascribed (acquired at birth, for example gender, race or class) or achieved (attained through individual talent or effort).

- **Social role** – once accorded a social status the individual is expected to conform to the culturally prescribed behaviour attached to the status (considered in more detail in Chapter 4).

- **Social networks** – these focus on the relationships between people; they are a set of links or connections with others. Early in the individual's life such links are established with family members. Later, links are made with peers and eventually colleagues. For instance, nurses network with other nurses and midwives with other midwives. Networks provide information, influence, potential for new relationships and opportunity for the sampling of cultural styles as well as access to money, power or status.

As well as such structures the definitions given thus far have also alluded to the consistent presence of cultures within societies. Culture is durable and persists over time. It is made up of societal aspects which are socially learned together with those aspects of society that are represented symbolically.

Culture can be described in terms of material and non-material aspects. Material aspects include objects, technology and the products of the arts. Non-material culture will include language, knowledge, skills, values, beliefs, customary practices and other symbolic forms of representation.

Values influence both norms and laws and in any given situation there may be more than one underlying value. Societies tend to have conflicting values – for example, whether health care should be provided locally or whether a district-based service is more desirable. The potential conflict between personal values and professional action is addressed in Chapter 3. But even where intra-cultural value conflicts exist, there is often the tendency still to see one's own values as superior to those of other societies. This inward focus is known as **ethnocentrism** and within this frame of thought any divergence from one's own values is seen as unnatural, inferior or wrong. The opposite perspective is known as **cultural relativism**. Assessment of cultural practices is based on their effectiveness within the culture of focus, in other words, their fitness for purpose. No practice is inherently good or bad, right or wrong.

Different subcultures may exist within a society. One definition of a subculture is that of a distinct social group within society which, while being related to the dominant culture, has its own values, attitudes, behaviours and lifestyles. Nursing and midwifery are subcultures within our society as are the differing lifestyles of the diverse ethnic groups. We live in a multicultural society.

The existence of subcultures identifies the presence of cultural variation, both between and within societies.

Why do you think this variation exists? Make a note of the areas that you believe are the key precipitants of variance.

Persell (1990) suggests that there are three possible explanations for cultural variation:

1. *The Ecological View* – suggests that societies adopt cultural practices that enable them to adapt to their particular environment. Thus climate, the availability and nature of food and water supplies, and the presence or absence of enemies have generated specifically appropriate cultural practices.

2. *The Functionalist View* – maintains that cultural variations exist because they serve different functions in the society. Functionalists assume that a society tends to maintain its equilibrium and that the restoration or maintenance of equilibrium is facilitated by various cultural elements. Cultural change occurs when society's functioning requires it.

3. *The Marxist View* – focuses on the inequality between groups in society. Dominant groups have been established who advance their own interests via cultural ideas and values. This culture creation enables some

groups in society to dominate others. Cultural change occurs as a result of class conflict, contradictions and adaptation, as forms of economic production change.

The health arena provides some good examples of cultural variation. Illness is treated differently both within different countries and also by differing groups within a given society. A particular ailment may be treated by witchcraft, prayer, radiation, chemotherapy, surgery or herbal remedies depending on where you live and the primary culture of influence.

Similarly, death occurs for a variety of reasons. In developing countries people may succumb to tuberculosis, starvation, typhoid, diphtheria or parasites. In contrast the main killers in industrialised nations are cancer, heart disease and cerebral vascular accident.

Cultural variation is also closely correlated with the rate of cultural change. Accelerated cultural change, as occurred during the Industrial Revolution in the United Kingdom, will introduce variance both within societies and between them. Sources of cultural change include:

- Structural changes – for example, demographic and economic changes.
- Inventions – often produced by combining existing cultural elements in new ways.
- Discovery – unearthing something which exists but which is not yet known.
- Diffusion – contact with different cultures is likely to result in the spread of useful inventions and discoveries.
- Cultural imposition – cultures may be imposed by one group on another, as when invading armies settle in a new land.
- Cultural revolution – the imposition of culture on others which may result in resistance or opposition from those others.

B F Skinner presents a picture of cultures which accords quite closely with that offered by ecologists and functionalists. He believes that cultural practices evolve and are strengthened when they have survival value. Culture both shapes and maintains the behaviour of those who are subject to it. Cultures only evolve when new practices which strengthen their existence are tested, approved and adopted. A key point is the development of cultural practices which not only reinforce the existing cultural framework but which also prompt members of the culture to actively work for its survival (Skinner, 1971).

Skinner's view of society is a heavily deterministic one. He argues that individual behaviour is primarily the result of contingent reinforcers in the environment. Individual agency is given short shrift; behaviours are learned not created. This is a view central to behavioural psychology, of which Skinner is a key figure.

While culture influences us, however, we are also able to shape its direction. As human beings we have the capacity for self-reflection and consequently do not always accept cultural norms blindly. The presence of numerous subgroups in society brings about cultural diversity and thus provides alternatives, so cultural determinism is not all-pervasive; cultural features may be changed by conscious actions.

The issue of agency versus structure is central to societal understanding. For individualists who argue for the primacy of agency, it is the actions of and choices made by individuals which create a given societal form. On the other hand, structuralists emphasise the importance of structures within society, arguing that individual actions and choices are the result of, rather than the precipitators of, those structures. An equally valid argument, though, is the one that proposes that the ideas, beliefs, reasons and standards of appropriateness of people cannot be considered in isolation from the social structures which they generate. People act on reason and are capable of defining purpose for their actions. Thus they can also be considered capable of making choices about alternative institutions and organisations. As the Open University succinctly states:

> Society should not be seen as exclusively constraining since it makes possible the development of our most fundamental capacities as human beings – e.g. to live and co-operate with others, and to make rational choices.

OPEN UNIVERSITY, 1986

The interaction between individual action and social forces can be illustrated by the following analogy supplied by Persell (1990). Social factors may be thought of as currents in a sea and on occasion these are irresistible; the person is carried along without choice. Sometimes the person may be able to swim across the current, directly against it or with it to improve their position. Some swimmers gain advantage through natural ability or training. Others may band together to construct vessels to help resist the current.

Social Order and Social Change

Social order is maintained by vast numbers of people adjusting their behaviour to one another; this is the process of **socialisation**. However, the possibility of social change is ever-present, either as a gradual process or as a result of violent revolution.

How is it that societies maintain continuity?

Why don't they more frequently degenerate into anarchy or chaos?

What serves to maintain social order?

Sources of social order include:

- **Rules for social conduct** – reflected in public concern over rule-breaking;

- **Coordinated economic activity** – for example manipulating behaviours through pricing mechanisms;

- **Social structure** – divisions of class, race or gender. Such structures serve to maintain existing patterns of distribution of power, wealth and opportunity. In addition, people are placed within a position in society – there is a place for everyone and everyone knows their place;

- **The state** – which makes rules and enforces them and maintains an administrative system. The state also performs an important symbolic function, as it provides the focus for national identity and ideological agreement;

- **Mass communication;**

- **Education system** – both this and the mass media perform a socialising role, passing on core values and dominant views;

- **Patterning of sexual and family life;**

- **Communities** – these serve to mediate between the individual and society at large and comprise a number of bonds:

  1 territorial bond (the area of residence)

  2 psychological bond (a sense of belonging)

  3 sociological bond (shared interests);

- **Social networks** – the communication links between members/groups/institutions/communities in a society;

- **Shared culture** – e.g. language, lifestyle, material and non-material artefacts;

- **Shared interpretation of social reality** – that is, the dominant view;

- **Shared values** – the core values, for example, of justice and equality.

Social order is also closely associated with **social control**. Social control refers to the systematised and patterned ways in which society prompts people to act predictably and desirably through guiding and restraining their behaviours.

An essential means of social control is the process of socialisation which will be considered later in this chapter. Interactionists believe that the rules of social control are negotiated in social interactions. Thus social control does not simply exist; it emerges through interaction. Norms and rules are constructed as they are applied.

Yarrow *et al* (1955) found that the wives of mentally ill husbands sought to view the erratic behaviour of their partners as normal until they reached a point where they could no longer cope. At this point the behaviour became redesignated as abnormal. Thus the definition of mental illness (its norm) changed according to the behaviours shown and the wives' ability to deal with those behaviours. However, while the above listed sources of social order and control maintain the continuity of societies, social change is also made possible by other factors.

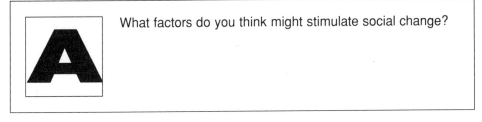

What factors do you think might stimulate social change?

Social changes are those structural and cultural changes in society which impact on large groups of people, particularly groups of people possessing a similar status and role in the society concerned.

As people develop from child to adult they, for example, go through education, become employed, leave the family home, get married and eventually die. However, these are all personal changes which will have little impact on the structure of society. The continuity of society remains despite a myriad of individual change processes.

True social change operates at a macro, rather than individual, level. The growth of the status of women in many societies and the transition from an agrarian economy to an industrial one during the Industrial Revolution of the eighteenth and nineteenth centuries are examples of social change.

Technology, such as that used in the development of the motor car can have far-reaching social effects. Increased mobility has changed the nature of family networks and the production processes used in motor car manufacture have been widely adopted as standard by other manufacturing industries.

Institutions, customs and habits serve to maintain continuity, and threats to them tend to be resisted by individuals. Hence social change is invariably slow, but sometimes crises may effect change. Examples of such crises effecting change might include revolutions, economic depressions or inflation, wars, natural disasters, rapid influxes of migrants, changes in climate (e.g. global warming) or the advent of an outstanding innovator.

One of the prime factors which ensures continuity in our society is the process of **socialisation**; the power of socialisation to influence individual behaviour and lifestyle is considered next.

Socialisation

Booth acknowledges the controlling influence of socialisation when he states:

Socialisation is the process by which an individual born with behaviour potentialities of an enormously wide range is led to develop actual behaviour confined within the narrow range of what is customary for him [her] according to the standards of his [her] group.

BOOTH, 1975

This statement of Booth's not only recognises the potential constraints inherent in any given society but also illustrates again that human behaviour and characteristics are the result of the interaction between nature (genetic make-up) and nurture (our experience of the world).

Congalton (1976) adds that socialisation serves to prepare individuals for their social roles by making apparent group values and beliefs, skills and knowledge, appropriate emotional responses and situation parameters. Socialisation also ensures that culture continues by passing it on from generation to generation.

As we grow from children to adults we learn about the world around us. We are socialised in the sense that we learn the values of our social groups and the behaviour which is appropriate to those values. The most influential of these social groups is the family; for the young child what the rest of the family sees as good, bad, ugly or beautiful they will see also. Society will differentially reward desired or undesirable behaviours as appropriate (as mentioned earlier when we considered the work of Skinner) and hence the behaviour of individuals at times reveals considerable uniformity in similar situations. In Chapter 3 we show the research of Felicity Stockwell illustrating the use of differential reinforcement by nurses in order to influence the behaviour of 'good' or 'bad' patients.

Societal influences which bear on socialisation include the family, peers, peer groups, the education system (day care/nurseries and schools), communities, the mass media and religious/political/economic and legal structures. In addition class, race, gender and economic position all affect how individuals are socialised (more of this in Chapter 2).

Such influences offer first-hand experience and develop awareness of status differences, order and authority figures. Subcultural influences include a number of 'reference groups'. These provide such things as values and moral codes of conduct and help to mould a person's self-esteem (the caring professions are examples of reference groups, as are street gangs or the armed forces).

There is much agreement that the first two years of life are of vital importance to the person's personality, the ability to form relationships, and to social behaviour as an adult. Thus the first relationship is the prototype for all others, i.e. that between mother and child. This belief is inherent within psychodynamic psychology and gives rise to the humorous adage that when an adult with problems contacts a psychoanalyst the first question asked of that adult will always be 'Tell me about your mother'.

Piaget and Freud both focused on childhood as a period of primary importance in the individual's life. Kohlberg and Erikson developed the ideas of Piaget and Freud and applied them to the social world. They indicated that socialisation is a lifelong process.

See Chapter 3 of Pennington D C (1986) *Essential Social Psychology*. London: Edward Arnold

and Atkinson et al (1990) *Introduction to Psychology* 10th Edition, pp. 77-99, 108, 511–518 and 80–85. London: Harcourt Brace Jovanovich Inc for greater detail of the works of Kohlberg, Erikson, Freud and Piaget.

THE INDIVIDUAL IN SOCIETY

'Tell me about your mother.'

As children we spend long periods in association with our parents in a relationship that is both dependent and developmental. Parents socialise us in order that we may integrate within our society.

 Reflect on what you have learned from your parents. How might this learning benefit you in the future? What particular aspects might be useful within a caring profession?

The following aspects will all be useful and no doubt you will have identified many more:

- Acting appropriately within the social context;

- Assessing the behaviour of self and others;

- Knowing when to succumb to the influence of others (to authority, with discretion, recognising greater skill or knowledge, or empathising with patient/client needs);

- Knowing when to attempt to influence others (for example within the health education arena).

Parents also provide a nurturing environment and essential social contact. Reported cases of children deprived of normal social contact note the presence of learning disability and either unsocial or antisocial behaviour.

This is illustrated vividly in an account of the life of Genie who, when discovered in the United States of America in 1970 at the age of 13, had spent over 11 years of her life in social, emotional and physical deprivation. This deprivation left Genie physically and emotionally undeveloped and unsocialised to the world around her. The lack of socialisation was exhibited in strange interpersonal relationships and behaviours such as urinating in unacceptable places. Despite intervention Genie ended up in an institution and her language abilities never progressed beyond those of a healthy four-year-old child.

This account describes a severe case of deprivation and subsequent lack of socialisation. It emphasises the importance of the socialisation process to effective human development and also serves to remind us that the development of intelligence, or the presence of learning disability, in an individual is not merely the outcome of inherited characteristics. The interaction between both inherited potential and the environment is the crucial determinant of a person's ability to integrate fully within society; to internalise societal norms, values and roles.

Social contact is essential to humans; just how essential is illustrated by Genie's story and numerous other researched examples such as that of René A Spitz (1945), who investigated infants raised in conditions of similar physical provision (well fed, clean environment, sufficient clothing, comparable health care) but with differing degrees of human contact. One group of babies was little stimulated and, because there were so many of them, got little personal attention. The other group of infants received lavish care and attention within a highly stimulating environment. Spitz's work suggested that the latter group developed faster and further physically, emotionally and socially. In fact, a quarter of the babies in the 'deprived' group died before they reached three months of age, apparently from lack of social contact.

Nurses and midwives might like to reflect on such research when deciding whether 'talking to patients/clients' is 'real' nursing; whether nursing is only expressed in physical activity.

Other research evidence exists to illuminate the importance of social contact. Harlow's experiments with young monkeys point to the importance of adequate social stimulation from key people; in this research instance the 'mother'.

See Atkinson et al 1990 *Introduction to Psychology.* (10th Edition) pp. 88–89. London; Harcourt Brace Jovanovich Inc. for an exploration of Harlow's experiments.

Just as the body will not mature physically without the physical exercise provided by the physical environment, nor will psychosocial maturation be possible without social interaction with other people.

Work that mind

Through socialisation we establish the 'significant others' in our lives and this in turn facilitates the development of the concept of self; a self-image. Predictable responses from both 'significant others' and those considered less significant give one a sense of identity, security and prior expectations about the behaviour of others. These stable elements in turn enable the individual to construct a picture of their place in society, and of themselves. At each stage in the lifespan (childhood, adolescence, adulthood) there are new norms to learn for adequate socialisation to occur. Significant others may change as well as the concept of self. Socialisation is thus a lifelong process.

Socialisation	Resocialisation
Socialisation is toward something – usually new, such as skills, rewards, position or status. The chosen goal is desirable to the individual concerned. Any costs incurred may be covered by the person concerned.	Resocialisation is away from something – usually of an undesirable nature such as solvent abuse or antisocial behaviour. Often the existing behaviours are preferred over the set of goals, and subjects rarely bear any personal costs.
The individual understands the connection between process and outcome and the process itself is attractive to the participant.	The connection between process and outcome may be unclear with the process itself causing physical, emotional or social distress.
The result is a fairly high success rate.	Failure in the process is more common than success.

Table 1.3. Socialisation and resocialisation

The norms of the large mental health and learning disability institutions which provided care prior to the drive for provision of services in the community during the 1980s and 1990s denied people social experiences outside the institutions themselves. Effective socialisation could not take place in such environments, consequently leaving many of the residents of these institutions ill-prepared for life in mainstream society. However, other factors, such as the individual's inherent abilities, are as important as the living environment. (Further consideration is given to the effects of institutions in Chapter 4.)

As the client/patient is socialised within society so must they be within the ward. The subculture of the ward will necessitate the learning of new group values and necessary roles. This initiation into the ward culture can be assisted by the nurse/midwife explaining ward functioning early in the admission process.

 Reflect on your experiences as a nurse/midwife. How long has it taken you to adjust to your professional role, to the culture of the wards? Think how difficult this experience must be for the client/patient who, due to the increasing brevity of in-patient treatment, might only have a week, or two weeks, to adjust to the hospital culture.

This adoption of 'new' cultural norms can be interpreted as 'resocialisation'. Institutions such as hospitals and prisons aim to 'resocialise' people. So too do the nurses, psychiatrists, psychologists, social workers and therapists who work within such institutions. Nurses and midwives are professional agents of socialisation and social control. The rehabilitative process can also be thought of as one of 'resocialisation'. The key differences between socialisation and resocialisation are listed in Table 1.3.

Social learning theory has arisen from consideration of socialisation emphasising as it does the role of people in the socialisation process. However Table 1.3 suggests that certain factors are likely to either help or hinder the effectiveness of social learning. For example, the teaching of social skills to a person with a learning disability or intransigent mental health disorder may be hampered by the existence in that person of conflicting values, beliefs, behaviours and skills. Alternatively, the acquisition of language can be seen as 'socialisation for something new' and therefore has an enhanced chance of success (more of language in Chapter 5).

The grief of death may in some part be due to the resocialisation process which has to be endured by the remaining friends and colleagues. Counselling involves coming to terms with loss as well as facing a new life.

It may seem that socialisation is something that is imposed on the individual, a process over which we have little control. However while they are being socialised, individuals themselves act as socialising agents. The parent shapes the child but the child also shapes the parent. We are not merely passive in the process.

Earlier mention was made of the primary role that the family plays in the socialisation process. Booth (1975) projects this familial role into the health arena in pointing out that where haphazard socialisation processes exist in a family the result may be an individual ill-prepared for their future role in society which may, in turn, result in mental illness.

Family therapy seeks to redress this imbalance through a focus on the familial relationships. The mental health service provider thus becomes an institution of socialisation, performing a role previously missing in the person's life.

> *Societies can be pretty inventive at producing new institutions that will socialise the failures from other organisations.*
>
> BOOTH, 1975

In summary, then, the socialisation process enables the individual to adopt status and the accompanying role behaviour. To perform each role adequately it is necessary to acquire habits, beliefs, attitudes and needs. Socialisation also helps individuals to understand their primary group and subculture and their place in the wider strategy.

Social change requires socialised individuals to change. For example, in times of prosperity norms of spending and materialism might be emphasised whilst in recessionary periods norms of providence, economy and conservation are encouraged.

We now move on to consider the issues of **conformity** and **compliance**. What is the difference between the two and how do they influence individual behaviour?

Conformity and Compliance

We have seen how the process of socialisation may lead one to conform to societal expectations for behaviour and interpersonal relationships. This section seeks to explore further the nature of conformity and how it may differ from that of compliance.

Conformity

Conformity may be defined as a situation in which group pressure, whether real or imagined, causes behavioural or belief change.

Both Sherif (1936) and Asch (1955) have demonstrated the influence of group pressure on individual conformity.

See Pennington DC (1986) *Essential Social Psychology* pp. 198–205. London: Edward Arnold, for descriptions of the work of Sherif and Asch.

Conformity may be expressed in both personal and social action. We may conform to many of society's expectations within our own homes (despite no apparent pressure to do so) as well as when mingling with groups of other people. For example, how many people have you invited for breakfast as opposed to dinner? Probably not many – if at all. Why should this be the case? One answer might be that we, as a society, consider such unpredictability to be undesirable. We actively seek predictability and associated dependability from individuals. These traits are expressions of the desirability and ease of conforming. Conformity allows us to interact with others, knowing in advance how they are likely to behave. The fact that much of the time people conform to the expectations of others promotes orderliness in society.

Do you think this is a reasonable explanation for conformity?

Might there be other reasons?

Why might you as a nurse or midwife conform to the wishes of the care team?

Pennington cites the work of Festinger (1954) who believes that conformity may be explained by social comparison theory. That is, we look to others for guidance in novel situations (the student nurse/midwife watches and seeks advice from the experienced nurse/midwife in new treatment situations).

Alternatively, we may conform to please other people, to avoid creating dissent or to avoid conflict with others. Additionally, people tend to feel uncomfortable and highly self-conscious if they are conspicuous in a crowd. Being overly self-aware may cause people to focus only on their failings and shortcomings. Thus there are three possible explanations of conformity, being:

1 Social comparison

2 Conflict avoidance

3 Self-awareness

Congalton (1976) argues that for order to be present in society conformity is essential and that those means by which conformity is produced can be collectively termed **social control**.

Conflict between individual needs and drives can be reduced by societal norms for behaviour. At times the need to feel a unique sense of identity conflicts with the need to obey or comply with others' wishes, prevailing norms or standards. This sets up the dichotomy of conformity and conflict.

Social norms, as mentioned above, suggest how people ought to behave; that is, they suggest how to conform. Four kinds of norms can be identified, each suggesting different degrees of conformity.

1 **Folkways** – are social customs to which people generally conform but for which there is no real obligation. Examples include wearing coordinated clothing, shaking hands on meeting or the wearing of a particular uniform by the nurse or midwife. Transgressions of folkways may result in people being labelled 'odd' or 'eccentric' but do not usually cause moral outrage.

2 **Mores** – are strongly held social norms, violation of which excites strong public reaction and often legal sanctions. Examples of such violations would include walking naked along your local street or abusing patients/clients in your care.

3 **Laws** – are norms that have been formally enacted by a political body.

4 **Taboos** – are prohibited social practices which are the strongest form of social norm. Incest is one example in our society, as is compulsory euthanasia for people once they reach the end of their productive working life.

These social norms are backed by sanctions; rewards for desired behaviour or penalties for those behaviours which are undesired.

Negative sanctions include gossip, social ostracism, the death penalty, fines or disapproving looks. Positive sanctions might include smiles, compliments, prizes, money or material goods. Social values provide the bedrock for norms. The complex nature of modern society challenges our understanding and we turn to 'experts' for answers. We conform to the experts' answers because we rely on them for help in interpreting our social world.

 Are there any parallels with this 'expert' view within nursing or midwifery? Make a note of your thoughts.

Quite clearly patients and clients depend on the 'expert' nurse or midwife for information about, and understanding of, their care and the applicable cultural norms of the care environment. Thus health professionals exercise great power over the degree of conformity of their patient/client groups.

Information can be deliberately manipulated to maintain status, power relationships and conformity or freely given to the individual concerned to facilitate conformity via informed consent.

Similarly, the qualified nurse/midwife exercises powers of conformity over junior/unqualified colleagues. The expert practitioner enables the novice to find meaning and understanding in the complex healthcare environment. But abuse of such expertise may lead the novice to challenge the norms of conformity and the validity of the 'expert' to prescribe such norms. The cloak of expertise is easily torn by abuses of power, poor role modelling and outdated methodologies.

We may have given the impression up to this point that conformity is an all-or-nothing situation – you either conform or you don't. Obviously the situation is not as clear-cut as that and degrees of conformity may exist.

What factors might be expected to affect conformity?

Note your responses to this question.

You may have been able to generate a comprehensive list and probably will have considered the following important factors:

- Whether responses are made in private or publicly;

- The attractiveness of the group which is the source of conformity;

- The power of relevant reference groups;

- Your level of self-esteem;

- The numbers of people in a group conforming in a given direction;

- The presence, or absence, of positive reinforcement of conforming action; conformity is highest when individuals are rewarded for agreement.

The nature of the social role adopted is important. Chapter 4 examines social roles in some depth but for the present purpose, suffice to say that when a person takes on a role they also take on the norms and expectations of behaviour associated with that role. One effect of role adoption may be the replacement of individual identity with group or role identity; the person is offered anonymity. This anonymity is also considered in Chapter 4 in the context of the institution and the effects such anonymity may have on the behaviours of carers and clients/patients. Mention is also made of the 1973 experiment of Haney, Banks and Zimbardo who demonstrated the power of roles to replace personal and ethical standards within a simulated prison environment.

Individual personality seems to play some part in the degree of conformity exhibited. Most of us seem to find a reasonable balance between uncritical acceptance of norms and complete rejection of them. However, there are a few individuals who seem deliberately perverse while others are extremely suggestible. A combination of anxiousness, need for approval and low self-esteem may result in an individual particularly susceptible to social influence. Characteristically, conformers tend to be:

- over-accepting
- submissive
- narrow in their range of interests
- inhibited
- rigid
- slow
- vacillating in decision-making
- confused and disorganised under stress
- over-anxious
- over-responsive to the evaluations of others
- restrictive with their children

Alternatively, non-conformers are:

- efficient
- capable
- self-reliant
- persuasive
- good leaders
- advisers
- active and vigorous in work and hobbies
- natural
- unaffected
- relaxed
- permissive with their children

 Do you feel that you neatly fit either of these groups? Given that the non-conformist characteristics are arguably the more positive of the two sets, does this mean that non-conformism is to be favoured over conformism?

Compliance

Compliance differs from conformity in that it operates at the individual rather than the group level. While conformity involves group pressure to change behaviour towards a group or social norm, compliance can be explained as an individual response to the use of request as a direct means of influence.

Four variables can be seen to affect compliance:

1 **Reciprocation** – Pennington cites the work of Regan (1971) as demonstrating reciprocation through findings that indicated that greater compliance is found in individuals who have previously received a favour than in a control group who have not.

2 **Foot-in-the-door technique** – a large request is more likely to be acceded to if it is preceded by a smaller request of a similar nature. Freedman and Fraser (1966) are cited by Pennington as believing that people feel helpful after complying to a small request and seek to be consistently helpful, leaving them compelled to accede to the large request. Alternatively, Pennington also introduces the work of Cialdini (1975) who suggests that an unreasonably large request which is followed by a more reasonable one which you really wish the person to comply with is likely to result in success for the latter. This is known as the 'barter' approach.

Might such knowledge assist you in gaining the cooperation of patients/clients in care programmes?

3 **Transgressions** – Pennington describes the work of Wallace and Sadella (1966) who found that people caught in the act of doing something wrong complied more to subsequent requests than those people who had transgressed but had never been caught.

4 **Self-esteem** – Apsler (1975), as outlined by Pennington, describes how the lowering of self-esteem, by getting individuals to say and do foolish things, can result in high levels of compliance. He suggests that this occurs in an attempt to recover loss of face. Chapter 4 addresses the almost unquestioned compliance that may be induced in clients by institutional processes which lower self-esteem.

Pennington also illuminated the distinction between public compliance and private acceptance (internalisation) using the work of Kelman (1958).

Public compliance involves the person in public conformity to group norms while privately maintaining a different opinion. There is said to be **normative** pressure to conform. Conversely, internalisation requires the person to believe that the group is correct and also to share that belief personally. Conformity is also motivated by **informational** pressure. Generally, informational pressure to conform is more associated with situations where there is a high degree of ambiguity, while the least ambiguous situations or tasks lend themselves to normative pressure.

Forced compliance may also be present, this being similar to public compliance but involving higher degrees of external pressure to conform. Compliance can be ensured either by punishment or the threat of it, or reward or the promise of it. However, a state of dissonance will exist between the individuals' overt behaviour and their private opinion. High levels of reward can serve to reduce dissonance by balancing high dissonant factors with high consonant (reward) elements.

In summarising this section, then, we have seen conformity is a group-focused phenomenon while compliance is more individually based. Conformity can be seen positively for as McGhie (1973) states, the individual is able to experience 'belongingness' and acceptance within the group through the use of conforming behaviour.

However, caution must be exercised in blindly conforming to all practices. In Chapter 4 conformity is addressed through consideration of Sykes' and Matza's **'techniques of neutralisation'** (Martin, 1984). These are formalised 'excuses' used by carers to justify conforming to the ill-treatment of patients/clients. Similarly, the word of the expert cannot always be justification for conformity. Consider the following illustration of the use of expert power as a final point in this section on conformity and compliance.

The systematic killing of millions of people as part of Hitler's so-called 'Final Solution' during World War II is now widely condemned and abhorred. However McGhie (1973) notes the experiment conducted by Mansson at the University of Hawaii in which two thirds of a group of five hundred students were persuaded by an expert discourse on strategies to deal with the problem of the mentally ill and emotionally unfit to accept the use of euthanasia or mercy killings. Thus the advocacy of programmes very similar in nature to those of Hitler's Nazi Germany but presented as scientific activity was sufficient to ensure high degrees of conformity in the student body.

Social Control and Social Conflict

Social Control

We have been considering how it is that individuals can be induced to conform to societal norms for behaviour. Considering the elements that encourage conformity from a macro perspective leads us on to examination of social control. Social control focuses on how individuals within a given group, subculture or society are persuaded to conform to the expectations of those social groupings.

To a great extent social judgement is a function of past experience, present and anticipated influence; the extent of that influence reflects social control.

Significant influences on social control include:

- **Verbal and non-verbal communication** – provide the potential for social control through the power of the medium. Think of the effect of a disapproving look or a threatening gesture on your behaviour. Chapter 5 explores this area in greater detail.

- **Organisations** – may exercise social control by issuing statements indicating how members should behave. For example, the United Kingdom Central Council's *Code of Professional Conduct for the Nurse, Midwife and Health Visitor* (UKCC, 1992) both facilitates action and constrains it within set parameters.

- **Laws** – these represent the formal aspect of social control.

- **Authority and authority figures** – authority may be exercised at an individual/personal or institutional level.

Milgram's classic experiments in the 1960s investigated both situational and social factors affecting people's willingness to obey authority (Milgram, 1963, 1965).

See Pennington D C (1986) *Essential Social Psychology* pp. 209-213. London: Edward Arnold,

or Atkinson et al (1990) *Introduction to Psychology* (10th Edition) pp. 737–741 London: Harcourt Brace Jovanovich Inc.

for accounts of Stanley Milgram's experiments.

Strong influences on obedience include the legitimacy of authority figures and the proximity of such figures. People must perceive authority figures to be legitimate in order to obey them and are more likely to obey such figures at a close, rather than a remote distance. Conflicting authority figures reduce levels of obedience, as do rebellion or resistance. Support from peers for rebellion or resistance further reduces individual willingness to obey.

Nurses and midwives will experience social control from:

- the nursing/midwifery hierarchy

- peers

- external influences present in their private and public lives (present at work as well as outside it)

The patient's/client's ability to adjust to the subculture of the hospital will be a reflection of prior social control. For example, the person who has learnt to be modest within their external lifestyle will experience discomfiture at undressing in front of others or eliminating in an environment with less privacy than is customary for them. Thus adjustment to the 'new' culture may prove difficult.

Certain expressions of social control may prove to be even more restrictive in their application. For, as Congalton (1976) identifies, doctors around the world are beginning to practise in a defensive manner to avoid being sued by an increasingly litigious patient group. Hence innovation, creativity and developments in treatments are potentially hampered by the growth of a litigious society which acts as a form of social control.

Social Conflict

Restrictive social control, as well as inadequate socialisation, may lead to social conflict. Conflict can be reduced however, if both parties can understand a little of how the other is thinking, how the other perceives the world and how their thoughts and perceptions influence their behaviour.

This emphasises the importance of understanding the roles of others in the multidisciplinary team; to be able to empathise with their positions. Students of nursing and midwifery often see 'management studies' as irrelevant to their stage of learning. Such studies, however, serve not only to provide beneficial knowledge and competencies but also to enable understanding of the manager's frame of reference. Such illumination may assist in reducing future conflict.

Based on your experience of life in our society, attempt to identify the main areas of social conflict. What activities, beliefs or values may serve to generate conflict?

The following areas are offered as worthy of consideration.

Political or economic conflict – Class struggles may be seen as a struggle over the spoils of economic activity – the relative shares involved. Much conflict in industrialised nations is of this nature. On a more personal level, the occupational re-grading of nurses and midwives during the late 1980s and early 1990s caused considerable conflict and subsequent appeal processes were long-drawn-out affairs. The potential for conflict exists when each year the Government decides the annual pay increases for public sector personnel. Often the expectations of personnel are not met by the proffered increase, an example occurring in 1993 when the Government imposed a one-and-a-half per cent ceiling on public sector pay increases.

Territorial conflict – Many of the armed conflicts scattered throughout the history of our world have been generated by the possession of, or the seeking to possess, territory. In recent times conflict has arisen in the former Yugoslavia, Kuwait and the Falkland Islands. Additionally the symbolic value attached to territory has seen conflict arise between Arabs and Israelis over Jerusalem and between Hindus and Moslems in India.

Ideological conflict – Ideologies are sets of beliefs, and conflict arises when a group fails to achieve the ideological goals of another. Conflict in Northern Ireland is ideological in nature and the tendency is for opposing group members to magnify the differences between themselves, thus increasing the severity of the conflict. Nurses and midwives are often drawn into ideological conflicts during their practice. Examples might include conflicts between the belief of the nurse/midwife in the preservation of life and the refusal of a Jehovah's Witness to receive a blood transfusion which may save his/her life. Similarly ideological conflicts may exist where the nurse is both the provider of care to an individual and an advocate for that person. Conflicts of interest may be readily apparent.

See Allmark P and Klarzynski R (1992) The case against nurse advocacy, *British Journal of Nursing* **2** (1), pp. 33–36.

Racial conflict – Biological difference, and its manifestations – for example, colour – is often the focus for strong intergroup conflict. However, such conspicuous badges of difference are often conveniently used to reflect political, ideological or territorial conflict. Greater consideration is given to conflict generated by racial and other societal divisions in Chapter 2.

Prestige conflict – Conflict is generated between groups in the seeking of superior status or prestige and the acquisition of concomitant power. The struggle for power is also very much to the fore in the other types of conflict outlined here.

Tension-release conflict – The five forms of conflict mentioned above are purposive in that they serve to achieve goals. Similarly, conflict may have a purpose in facilitating emotional release. The conflict situations experienced by soldiers returning from battle often enable the release of emotions generated by their traumatic experiences.

Conflict can provide the opportunity for cathartic release of emotional tension – especially if the conflict arena is managed by an impartial facilitator, as is the case in some individual and group therapies. Emotional release is an example of expressive social conflict, as is deflected hostility. Deflected hostility in a group setting may result in the tensions of one group being relieved through the 'scapegoating' of another. Consequently, nurses and midwives may attribute the blame for ineffective care to the patients/clients concerned ('They did not do what they were supposed to!'). Such deflection of hostility can reduce the levels of stress amongst the source-group members.

The individual and society conflict – Psychoanalytical theory assumes that conflict between individual needs and wants and societal provision is natural. Consequently, conflict between groups represents the shared reactions of group members to pressure from other sections of society. Psychoanalytical theory focuses on the successful resolution of conflict rather than the prevention of conflict precipitants. The emphasis is on the individual or group ability to make effective adjustments to the conflict situation.

Where people have diverse goals and differing abilities or opportunities for goal achievement (see the discussion of life chances in Chapter 2) and where goals are desired by many, but only available to a few, social conflict is inevitable. However, such conflict makes possible the social structuring of human relationships, the result of which we call a society. Conflict cannot be eliminated but we can seek to understand it. Understanding on all sides is more likely to reduce conflict than unilateral understanding. Thus in problem-solving and decision-making, sharing of collective goals can assist the resolution of conflict. The acquisition of power through restricting the release of knowledge is a hindrance to effective multidisciplinary team functioning. Student nurses/midwives would benefit from being informed about what has to be done by the team to achieve collective goals, rather than being given directives for action without explanation of the purpose of the action.

The mediums of social control mentioned earlier in this section make easier the ordered resolution of conflict. That is, they allow society to change, develop and progress through conflict and challenge without complete disintegration of societal functioning during the change process. In the next section we consider a particular origin of social conflict in more detail – that is, the concept of **deviance**.

Deviance

Crime is . . . necessary.

DURKHEIM (1964)

This statement stems from a belief that determining what is 'right' is consequent to identification of what is 'wrong'. Major innovators such as Isaac Newton, Emily Pankhurst and Florence Nightingale were seen by many to be 'deviants' in their time, but without these people's differing beliefs, values, behaviour and approaches, successful social change would not have taken place in the manner that it did.

Illness may be seen as deviance within a society which places emphasis on health and the economic productive responsibility of the individual. Such illness, however, may be legitimised, and thus no longer exist as deviance, by the according to an individual of the 'sick role' and the individual's acting-out of the designated role.

Talcott Parsons (1972) identified four special features of the sick role:

1 During illness individuals are no longer held responsible for their behaviour as they no longer control their state of health.

2 This lack of responsibility in turn exempts the individual from some of the usual obligations. Occasionally the exemption is forced on the individual in a prohibitive or preventative form for the duration of the illness. The individual is prevented from carrying out some of his or her usual tasks or roles.

3 Sick people are obliged to recognise that being ill is undesirable and that they must try to 'get well'. This includes cooperation with those assisting in the recovery process and the legitimate sick role may be withdrawn if cooperation is withheld.

4 Sick people, and their families as appropriate, are required to seek competent help and to accept that help when it is made available.

 How might acceptance of the 'sick role' outlined above have an impact on both the patient/client and the care providers? Make a note of the key points.

Let us examine each facet of the sick role in turn:

The issue of deferred responsibility has been legally recognised in the differing approaches used to intervene in criminal acts involving those people with a mental illness (accorded the sick role) and those without (not accorded the sick role). While the former may be given access to therapeutic interventions the latter are usually not. For individuals with a learning disability it is arguable that being perceived as 'sick' in some way denied them social learning opportunities related to acquiring both rights and responsibilities. Carers within the field of learning disability may have inadvertently hindered individual development through tolerance of inappropriate behaviours acceded to through the deferring of individual responsibility. Thus, the acquisition of rights for people with a learning disability may not have been balanced with an allied awareness of responsibilities.

In a wider sense, deferred responsibility leads to nurses and midwives having to tolerate behaviour which would otherwise be unacceptable outside the care environment – and so instances of aggression and violence may be seen as 'part of the job' and not accorded adequate consideration within care delivery planning.

Conversely, acceptance by nurses and midwives of the nature of illness and its effects on patient/client behaviour can enhance the quality of care delivery. In developing systems of care which are patient/client-focused, health professionals are not only increasing the rights of patients/clients to determine the nature of their experience but also altering the responsibility ratio away from a passive, recipient patient/client to an active person who shares the responsibility for 'getting better' with the health provider.

Unfortunately, the exemption from responsibility has in certain instances become a restriction for the patient/client and encouraged deterministic approaches from carers. At one end of the spectrum this may involve patients feeling aggrieved at being denied the opportunity to return to work by a GP who feels they are not ready to do so. At the other extreme there may be a global restriction of opportunities and life-chances as experienced by some individuals residing within the large mental health and learning disability institutions during the first 80 years of this century.

The obligation to cooperate in 'getting well' and 'competent help' are interlinked facets. These facets may lead to the blind acceptance of professional values, beliefs and practices by patients/clients and the abuse of power accorded by the role of the professional practitioner. At its worst 'cooperation' involves unthinkingly following directives from care providers, acknowledged in Chapter 4 as a key indicator of **institutionalisation**. These components of the sick role may serve as justification of a professional presence (competent help) and reinforce the notion that only professionals know the 'right' approaches or the 'right' answers.

Another difficulty lies in the definition of 'illness' and its applicability across a range of situations influencing individuals. We have already mentioned the potentially erroneous application of the label 'ill' to people with a learning disability and people with mental health disorders.

In the earlier part of the century, illegitimate mothers and individuals who challenged societal norms fell into this category of 'ill'; many spent long periods of their lives in institutions as a result. Many individuals, the so-called anti-psychiatrists, such as Thomas Szasz, have challenged the notion of mental disorder as an 'illness', preferring to view the concept as a socially created entity. That is, it only exists because society defines it thus. Similar arguments exist in relation to the position of people with a physical disability in our society; they are disabled only by society's lack of provision for their needs, so that their disability is socially constructed.

Contemporary approaches indicate a shift by health professionals away from a focus on illness toward interventions based on health and holistic need-satisfaction models.

 Readers might like to investigate the 'sick role' further in the context of different approaches to treatment/care. *See* Stuart G W and Sundeen S J (1979) *Principles and Practice of Psychiatric Nursing*, Chapter 2, Conceptual Models of Psychiatric Care, pp. 16–38 (Role of Patient). London: CV Mosby Co.

Stepping outside the 'norms' of the sick role may serve to label the patient/client as 'deviant' in the eyes of the nurse/midwife. However the patient/client 'role' as described above, has changed over time, and as with major innovators, the patients/clients who pursue their own beliefs and behaviour may well be redefining the norms of the role. Hence successful social change within nursing and midwifery is inextricably linked with the needs and expectations of patient/client groups.

> *Deviance is always a matter of perspective; you can deviate only from a norm, and the norm, the expected behaviour, is that which is held to be so by the people concerned.*

CONGALTON, 1976

Qualified nurses and midwives will have expectations regarding student nurses and midwives, about norms appropriate for student nurses and midwives and what behaviour is tolerable. Behaviour from students that contravenes norms or levels of tolerance will be seen as deviant. However the student may operate under a different set of expectations or have different norms for behaviour. If this is the case social conflict will arise. As noted earlier, however, conflict can be expected in any socialisation process, qualified nurses and midwives being agents of socialisation for the next generation of nurses and midwives.

Why do you think individuals choose to deviate from the norm? What factors might encourage them in, or prevent them from, doing so?

Individual deviance is a balance of the strength of the person's inclination to deviate, the possibility of being caught, the strength of the barriers preventing deviance, the penalty for deviance and the likelihood of that penalty actually being enforced.

In addition, society employs tactics of prevention, prohibition and penalty. The nurse teaching social skills to a person with a learning disability is 'preventing' deviance from social norms in the future. The midwife requesting the mother not to smoke in the ward is exercising prohibition. Penalties may be applied by the United Kingdom Central Council for Nursing, Midwifery and Health Visiting (UKCC); for example, withdrawal from the register, in the case of professional misconduct. Similarly, the legal system makes widespread use of prevention, prohibition and penalty to maintain social order. Chapter 4 illustrates how institutions may so rigorously use these that all creativity and individual agency may be stifled.

You might like to reflect on how effective social control might be with the deviant nurse or midwife. Consider this in relation to:

1 prevention

2 prohibition, and/or

3 penalties or punishment

Deviance can be seen as a particular origin of social conflict but also more positively as the source of creativity and progress. It plays a role in society by both reinforcing the norms of the majority and providing for challenge which stimulates innovation.

The final section of this chapter examines **attitudes**: their function, nature and change, and their relevance to understanding humans and their behaviour.

Attitudes

Nurses and midwives will be continually confronted by the attitudes held by their patients/clients on a daily basis. Sometimes such attitudes will be shared, at other times they will be in conflict. The continued presence of attitudes cannot be ignored, nor their impact on the provision of effective care for health gain. Allport (1954) believes attitudes to be:

> . . . *the most distinctive and indispensable concept in social psychology.*
>
> ALLPORT 1954

Understanding attitudes is crucial to the understanding and explanation of individual behaviour as we constantly sample the attitudes of others, put forward our own points of view and try to change the opinion of others.

Now that's what I call an attitude! . . .

Defining Attitudes

Attitudes may be defined as the predisposition to respond in a constant manner to a given object, such predisposition having been learned at an earlier point in time. Four aspects of the definition which are central to the understanding of attitudes are:

- that experience provides the source for the learning of attitudes;

- that once learned, attitudes predispose behaviour;

- that both attitudes and behaviour are consistent in their manifestation;

- that whether responses are favourable or unfavourable is the result of the evaluative element of the attitude held.

Succinctly then, an attitude is a predisposition to think, feel and act towards some object, person, group or event in a more or less favourable or unfavourable way. This tripartite distinction of thought, emotion and behaviour is basic to a Componential Model of Attitudes espoused, within a Structural Approach, by Katz in 1960.

The Components of Attitudes

There is some agreement among psychologists that attitudes consist of three components, as follows.

1 **The cognitive component** – Beliefs about the attitude object – for example, 'oranges contain lots of vitamins'. Beliefs may be biased and not acquired directly. For instance, individuals who have never met persons of a particular race or social group may well be convinced that all Irishmen are stupid, or that all West Indians are only interested in sex and loud music however erroneous such a conviction. Such beliefs may well be formed solely on the basis of gossip, newspaper articles or television situation comedies, for example, and may eventually become resistant to change through direct experience. Chapter 3 examines how the sharing of a simplified, superficial view of the object of an attitude constructs a stereotype and how prejudging on the basis of that stereotype becomes a prejudice.

2 **The affective component** – Feelings and values about the attitude object – for example, 'I love oranges'. Individual feelings vary from person to person in intensity and may be of a positive or negative nature. Often this component is the most difficult to change as it tends to be the most deeply

rooted. This component reflects an evaluation of the attitude object; it tends to bring forth an evaluation along a good–bad or I approve–disapprove dimension.

3 **The behavioural/conative component** – Behaviour, or intent to act, with respect to the attitude object or person – for example, 'I eat an orange a day'. This component is better viewed as a predisposition to act rather than as a fixed certain response. It may not be exhibited if social pressure prevents it from appearing. It is a common finding that what people say and what they actually do often differs greatly, a situation often referred as **attitude/behaviour inconsistency**.

The structural approach of the componential model can be utilised to construct a process for attitude expression. This process begins with held *beliefs* and *values*, which serve to form *attitudes*, which in turn generate *intentions* that result in expressed *behaviour*.

However, while the componential model of attitudes facilitates the definition of the structures and processes of attitudes, it does not explain the reasons for their existence, that is, the functions that attitudes perform.

The Function of Attitudes

Why do people hold attitudes? What purpose do attitudes serve for the individual? How do you think attitudes facilitate your existence in society?

Attitudes form the means by which we structure our world, our experience. In order to cope with the continuous influx of new information provided by our senses, we need some means of ordering and classification. We need to know what to accept and what to reject, what to believe and what not to believe.

The student upon first entering nursing or midwifery training enters an alien world of complex behaviours and challenges. Attitudes are used to come to terms with complexity and challenge by acting as sieves or filters, cutting down the amount of new information needing processing and relating new information to that already possessed. As students on your first practice placement in nursing or midwifery, you may well have chosen to adopt the attitude: 'The qualified staff know what they are doing'. This would have enabled you to learn by example and follow instructions rather than to allow the new experience to overwhelm you. Additionally as new nurses or midwives you probably sought the approval of fellow group-members. One way of effecting this is to adopt the attitudes of the group – for example, 'our responsibility is to the care of other members of society', or 'we are not going to be swots'. A person is reinforced by the group for expressing the requisite attitudes, which may either be held at a superficial compliance level only or be deeply integrated within the individual's personality.

The functional approach, as outlined by Katz (1960), categorises the above ideas into four distinct functions served by attitudes.

1 **The adjustment/adaptive function** – This is concerned with the usefulness of attitudes in helping us to obtain rewards and avoid punishments; to achieve goals and avoid unpleasant situations. Thus nurses and midwives may identify with the attitudes of colleagues which enable them to function as effective practitioners and disregard those that hinder multidisciplinary team working.

2 **The knowledge function** – Here the assumption made is that people need to give adequate structure to their world and that attitudes serve that function. Individuals structure their worlds through use of information. Knowledge of the physical and social world makes it more predictable and reduces uncertainty. Chapter 3 considers the use of stereotypes in some detail; here, they serve to illustrate the knowledge function as their use helps simplify the social environment.

3 **The self-expressive/value-expressive function** – This emphasises the satisfaction derived from expressing attitudes appropriate to our personal values and to the concept of self. To have a sense of identity we need both to be self-aware and to have the ability to communicate such awareness to others. Therefore, nurses and midwives must be both self-aware and have the ability to communicate their values, beliefs and feelings in order to establish a professional identity.

4 **The ego-defensive function** – This refers to the way in which our attitudes defend our self-image; attitudes may act as protective shields both against ourselves and others. Attitudes enable us to avoid intense self-criticism which might destroy our self-image. For example, imagine the nurse or midwife who is working on a night shift who finds herself being short-tempered with patients/clients because of tiredness. This behaviour may induce feelings of guilt in the nurse/midwife. However if her usual attitude is caring, considerate and calm then the incident on night duty can be dismissed by the nurse/midwife as unrepresentative of her usual behaviour. Similarly, when dealing with threats to our ego (self-image, self-esteem) from others it is suggested that we may project our conflicts on to those others. This is sometimes the case with prejudice, as one's own faults and conflict origins are projected on to other people. The **ego-defensive** function implies therefore that the maintenance

of positive attitudes about ourselves serves to maintain a positive self-image.

Attitudes, then, allow us to make sense of the world around us, affirm our own worth and extract rewards from our environment. But where do they come from? Why do individuals have different attitudes? How are attitudes formed?

Attitude Formation

Ask yourself: Why do I hold the attitudes that I do? What aspects of my life might have influenced the development of my attitudes?

Who has been important in my life?

Have I always had my present attitudes or not?

You may well have felt that a number of elements have influenced the formation of your attitudes and you would be right in thinking so. The following factors are thought to be important in attitude-formation:

1   **Learning theories** – There is a clear link here with the process of socialisation; our attitudes are learned through classical and instrumental conditioning and the shaping behaviour of our parents. Children are not born with a predisposition to view religion, politics and other cultures in a specific way. They acquire their views over a considerable period of time. The nature of this acquisition may be explained by:

    (i)   **Conditioning** – Put simply, parents and others reward children for having the 'correct' attitudes and tend to criticise them for holding views which are at odds with their own, or those of society. Over a period of years the child generally takes on many of the attitudes of parents, older children, teachers, and other significant people in their lives through continuous exposure to reinforcement and punishment schedules. Within adolescence, though, there is often rebellion against parental and authority attitudes.

    (ii) **Modelling** – Attitudes can also be learned through **imitation** of, for example, parents, teachers, siblings and peers or through the process of **identification** identifying, for instance, with one's 'heroes' and adopting their attitudes.

    The nurse whose upbringing emphasises self-control and emotional coldness might well find it difficult, for example, to be empathic with an individual experiencing emotional instability as, perhaps, a result of a mental health disorder.

2 **Direct experience** – The individual accrues direct experience of the object or person, which or who forms the focus for the attitude. Baron and Byrne (1977) suggest that attitudes acquired in this way are stronger and more vivid than attitudes acquired indirectly or 'second-hand'.

3 **Individual expression** – Certain attitudes are held to be an indirect expression of personal problems of which the individual may not be entirely aware. People experiencing neuroses may form certain attitudes which allow them to express their own emotional difficulties. For example, investigations indicate that people who are the least tolerant of racial or religious differences are themselves generally emotionally unstable and neurotic in nature. Their intolerant attitude to certain sections of the community allows them to express their own inner insecurity and aggression.

Through a combination of these factors involved in attitude formation, people are selectively exposed to certain attitudes. For health professionals, research on attitude formation seems to indicate two main implications:

> *It is much easier to influence a person's attitude whilst it is being formed than to try and change it years later. Parents can have a very important influence on the development of their children's attitude towards health.*
>
> *Social learning theory has illustrated the importance of exposing children to appropriate models. Thus, the media has a significant role to play in transmitting health education, using characters that children respect and even idolise.*
>
> NIVEN, 1989

In the quotation above, Niven mentions the notion of change. The formation of attitudes and their subsequent change are inextricably linked, as formation is itself a change-process. For instance, the forming of rock structures is the result of long periods of ecological change. Some of the factors involved in attitude formation can also prove of use in attempting attitudinal change at a later date.

Attitude Change

Each day we are subjected to an onslaught of attempts to try to change our attitudes to all sorts of things. Advertisements implore us to buy certain products or services, politicians plead with us for our vote and the Health Education Authority attempts to persuade us to give up smoking and take more exercise.

The functional approach to attitudes suggests certain implications for attitude change. That is, the change agent must know both the attitude held and the function served by that attitude. Approaches to attitude change must therefore match the function. So, for example, an attitude serving a knowledge function might be changed by the introduction of new information, but such an approach would be unlikely to change an attitude serving an ego-defensive function.

Television, radio, magazines and newspapers are all mediums of communication used to promote some attitudes and decry others. Communication can play a key role in attitudinal change, especially persuasive communication.

Persuasive Communication

Janis and Hovland (1959) have investigated the effect of persuasive communication on attitude change, focusing on the source (the communicator), the message (characteristics of the communication) and the audience (target/recipient) factors. Changes in opinions, perceptions, evaluations and behaviour were used as measures of attitudinal change. Janis and Hovland proposed the following (summarised in Figure 1.2):

1 Source factors influenced the attention paid to the communication and thus could alter attitudes;

2 Message factors influenced audience comprehension of the message; and

3 Audience factors impinged on the acceptability of the attitude change to the audience.

If you were attempting to change an attitude held by a patient/client by persuasive communication, what:

- source factors (characteristics of yourself)

- message factors (the presentation and content of the communication) and,

- audience factors (characteristics of the patient/client)

would need consideration? Note your answers as they will also prove to be of use when studying Chapter 5.

These findings imply the following:

- Health professionals, as source factors, must appear credible, have an appearance that maximises likeability and put across their message in a clear, crisp fashion.

- The message must be strong. Emotional appeals may be made. If, for example, the emotion of fear is being used,

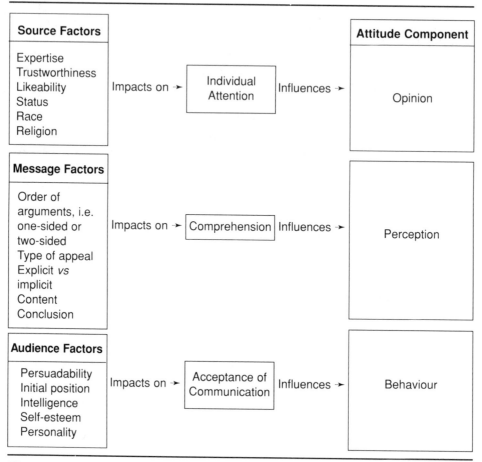

Figure 1.2. Persuasive communication and attitude change

individuals must believe that they are at risk, and they must also believe that if they heed the advice they will be in no danger. The type of argument used is also important. One-sided arguments can be used with 'friendly' audiences, but with indifferent or antagonistic audiences then it is better to present the opposing view and attack it successfully. Familiarity with the message, through repetition, can alter attitudes in a favourable direction.

- The personality characteristics of the audience, such as low self-esteem and high need for social approval, are thought to be related to ease of attitude change (Zellner, 1970). Cognitive explanations emphasise the ability of individuals to give counter-arguments and reactance (doing exactly the opposite) as important factors in resistance to change (Worchel and Brehm, 1971 in Pennington, 1986).

Reactance tends to occur when the individual feels that his/her freedom is being limited in some way.

Does this mean that hospital-wide bans on smoking are unlikely to succeed?

Our need to feel autonomous and make choices for ourselves causes us to resist changes which threaten these human attributes.

Finally, previous exposure to attempts to change attitudes can be important. Suppose, for example, two speakers were presenting the case for and against fluoridation of water. The first speaker has two options:

1 to give the best presentation possible for their case, or

2 to present an incompetent case for the 'other side'. This procedure 'inoculates' the audience against the next speaker. The audience responds to the bad presentation by rehearsing counter-arguments which are then 'fired' at the next speaker.

Another major approach to attitude change has centred on dissonance theory.

Dissonance Theory

This focuses on the relationship between attitude and behaviour. Pennington (1986) argues that individuals seek consistency between beliefs, values and attitudes. In addition attitudes and behaviours must be consistently matched as should different attitudes.

This organisation of attitudes, beliefs and behaviour is known as **cognitive consistency** and serves to underscore rational behaviour. Absence of cognitive consistency may be extremely uncomfortable for individuals. Bateson *et al* (1956) proposed that schizophrenia may be caused by inconsistency. That is, when one person regularly makes two simultaneous but inconsistent communications to another, schizophrenia may be the psychological response. This is Bateson's 'double-bind' theory, the recipient of the inconsistent communications does not know in which direction to act. While this might be an extreme example, it is suggested that people are motivated to reduce or avoid inconsistency whenever possible. There are a number of theoretical approaches to cognitive consistency such as Heider's Balance Theory (Heider, 1958) or Osgood and Tannenbaum's Congruity Principle (Osgood and Tannenbaum, 1955).

Interested readers may wish to pursue these further in:
Pennington D C (1986) *Essential Social Psychology*, pp. 67–71. London: Edward Arnold.

Another term used to describe cognitive inconsistency is **cognitive dissonance**. Dissonance can be defined as a 'negative drive state' that results from the individual holding two or more psychologically inconsistent cognitions (Festinger, 1957).

Festinger is closely associated with Cognitive Dissonance Theory and argues that the dissonance created by inconsistent cognitions motivates the individual to change behaviour or attitudes – to attain consonance (consistency). The individual who finds smoking pleasurable, but also knows that the habit increases the risk of lung cancer, may experience dissonance. Consonance can be achieved in this situation either by way of a change in behaviour or through a change in attitude. Festinger believes that individuals tend to change their attitude rather than their behaviour. A change in behaviour would require the individual to cease smoking. Alternatively, individuals can rationalise their behaviour (alter their attitude to avoid dissonance) by arguing that 'it will never happen to me' or 'my father smoked for 50 years and it never did him any harm'.

Dissonance may also occur when two equally attractive options are available – for example, the choice of buying a new car or going on an exotic holiday. In such a case, dissonance may be reduced by emphasising the positive aspects of one option and the negative aspects of the other.

Attitudes may be changed through contact with other people. There can be dissonance in relationships if two people who like each other have opposing viewpoints on certain topics. To resolve the dissonance the individuals tend to reduce the degree of polarisation in their attitudes and thus also to alter their behaviour.

It is sometimes difficult for nurses and midwives involved in health education to understand why some people do not take notice of professional advice, despite being presented with overwhelming evidence that their lifestyle is endangering their health or life itself. Dissonance, as we have seen, can impede the health professional, but it can also become an ally if correctly managed.

The available research on dissonance and persuasive communication can be used to work against disease processes such as Acquired Immune Deficiency Syndrome (AIDS). Initially consideration should be given to the characteristics of the target population (characteristics of the audience). Those at high risk of the disease need to be assessed in the context of their pursuit of 'unsafe' practices. It is often more effective to attempt to 'modify' behaviour rather than attempt to change it completely. This is the reasoning behind the recent health campaign on AIDS emphasising 'safe sex' – that is, the use of condoms – rather than trying to prevent sexual activity altogether. Similarly, drug users are provided with clean needles to prevent the spread of disease.

One of the main roles of health prevention is to convince people that they are at risk (characteristics of the communication). This is an ongoing problem within the prevention programmes for AIDS and their future success seems dependent on establishing the similarities between affected individuals and those who believe themselves not to be at risk. This has been illustrated with a latter emphasis on heterosexual sexual activity rather than focusing solely on gay relationships or drug users.

Cognitive consistency theories, then, predict that attitudes change when imbalance, incongruity or dissonance arises and that attitudes are often changed in order to be consistent with behaviour.

 Reflecting on the information already presented in this chapter can you identify any other potential means of changing attitudes?

A number of interlinked means of changing attitudes might be identified:

1 **Reward and punishment** – As attitudes can be formed by reward and punishment schedules so may they be changed. Alternatively the principles involved can be used to strengthen positive attitudes, creating opposition to the negative forms.

2 **Classical conditioning** – Many experiments have illustrated the impact of classical conditioning on attitude formation. Associating, or pairing, positive outcomes with given attitudes will strengthen the use of those attitudes or change towards them. For example, when Adolf Hitler blamed all of Germany's post-First World War economic and social problems on German Jews he was using a classical conditioning procedure. By continually associating the Jews with the very real ills of German society, Hitler produced strong anti-semitic attitudes. Conversely, he associated the Aryan race of Germans with strength and intelligence, thus engendering in the German peoples a positive attitude toward people with 'blond hair and blue eyes' – held to be characteristics of German Aryans.

3 **Imitation** – We have already discussed the influence of role models, and our imitation of these, within the section on Socialisation. For nurses and midwives, recognition of the influence of role models on attitude formation and change raises conscious awareness of the need to be effective role models for patients/clients.

4 **The mere exposure effect** – Attitudes may change with experience, even if this experience is not associated with good or bad events. It seems that merely being exposed to new material over a period of time makes it more pleasant.

5 **Ego involvement** – When people become personally involved in a project, attitude change is greater. This finding emphasises the need for people's active participation in health education in order to achieve maximum health gain.

6 **Role playing** – Ego involvement is facilitated by the use of role playing. Additionally, the technique allows people to understand the point of view of the other person and to be empathic. This can be a powerful tool for attitudinal change.

7 **Self-perception** We argue at numerous points in this book that self-awareness is an essential prerequisite for awareness of others. Darryl Bem (1967) indicates that people often change their attitudes because they watch their own behaviour.

8 **Education** – Health education attempts to ensure that the 'right' causes are attributed to health, or indeed illness. For instance, if an individual believes mental health disorders to be the outcome of 'sinning' (not an uncommon perception), they may also hold unfavourable attitudes toward people with mental health disorders. Education in the known aetiology of mental health disorders may well alter the attitude held to a more positive regard for the individual.

9 **Group norms** – As we have already stated elsewhere in this chapter there is a strong tendency for individuals to conform to whatever standards are set by their group. A person is rewarded for such conformity and sanctioned for non-conformity. For some people this pressure is so powerful that they conform to the attitudes of groups that they have never met or seen before. This principle underpins attitude change via group therapies, as used by bodies such as Alcoholics Anonymous or the Therapeutic Communities established to assist sociopaths.

10 **Social support** – Even a small amount of support enables an individual to adopt positive attitudes against group pressure. In real-life situations, a small band of people may oppose thousands, for example, in supporting their religious beliefs.

It might seem that because there is such a range of methods available to facilitate attitude change, such change is a foregone conclusion. But it is important to remember that attitudes can be changed only if the person holding the attitude is willing to have it changed. It seems worth while asking ourselves why we are trying to change a given attitude – for the benefit of the individual concerned or to make the situation easier for ourselves?

Attitudes cannot effectively be judged to be right or wrong. It may therefore be more appropriate to ask whether the attitudes a person holds are consistent with one another, with their associated beliefs, and with their associated actions. Health education attempts to ensure consistency between the components of attitudes by primarily targeting the cognitive and affective levels. Trying to alter behaviour alone often leaves individuals feeling directed, without the ability to exercise choice and without autonomy.

Nurses and midwives might benefit from asking themselves the following questions prior to seeking attitudinal change in patients/clients:

- Am I aware of my own attitudes?

- Do I know how these have developed?

- Can I perceive how my attitudes influence others?

- Can I modify my attitudes if necessary?

- Can I communicate necessary information to patients/clients without it becoming distorted by my own attitudes?

- What attitudes does the patient/client hold?

- How strongly held are these attitudes?

- Are their attitudes, or components of attitudes, consistent?

- Are patients/clients aware of their attitudes?

- What influences appear to have been important in the formation of the patient's/client's attitudes?

- Do they understand how their attitudes affect their behaviour?

- Are they aware of the effects of their behaviour on others?

- Do I think I can assist the patient/client in attaining attitude consistency if it is not present?

- Is the patient/client showing an interest in change?

- Is there any incentive for the patient/client to change?

- Are patients/clients capable of analysing their attitudes in the future and thus effecting change themselves?

Attitudes act together with other information the person receives, so that when illness becomes a possibility the person is ready to develop a theory of the illness. This theory is shaped by patients'/clients' bodily experiences, by the information received from external sources (such as the family doctor and television programmes) and by their personal experience of illness. The way in which this held theory of illness relates to the treatments, or care, perceived to be available from conventional health care services will affect whether the person uses the National Health Service system or alternative provider services, or does not pursue treatment options.

Whichever option is adopted in pursuing care and treatment, the nurse and midwife can expect the patient/client to arrive with pre-formed attitudes and expectations to which they will be expected to conform. Part of the individual assessment process will involve establishing exactly what these expectations are and the theory of illness which underpins them.

The Final Point

This chapter has attempted to address a wide range of factors which impinge upon human behaviour and which have relevance to the nurse's and midwife's understanding of the patient/client.

We have tried to describe how society and the processes of social order, social control and social change influence individual behaviour. Socialisation has been examined both as a key determinant of behaviour and as a process which facilitates the development of the person as an effective citizen within society.

People's behaviour may be expressed as forms of compliance or conformity or as the precipitants of social conflict and we specifically considered deviance in this context. Finally, we discussed attitude formation and change and the major effect that attitudes have on individual behaviour.

With all these factors we have attempted to bring out their significance to the nurse and midwife in the pursuit of maximum health gain for the patient/client. In examining the factors outlined above we have been drawing on the social sciences of psychology and sociology in what could be argued to be a reductionist, scientific manner. Farmer chooses to disagree with such an approach, particularly its use in shaping today's society. She believes that such preoccupation with rationality

> . . . has fashioned societies which create and tolerate mass starvation and major pollution, and which are further characterised by wars, uncontrollable inflation, mass unemployment, gross maldistribution of wealth, rampant racism, a rise in suicides and violent crime, and drug and alcohol misuse.
>
> FARMER, 1993

She goes on to argue that there is an alternative, that of the female world-view:

> which is intuitive, holistic and focused upon the observable phenomena of internal states.
>
> FARMER, 1993

Pelletier continues this theme in suggesting that:

> Out of the chaotic conditions of modern man has come a pressing need and an earnest quest for meaning and life goals beyond material saturation. Perhaps only when a certain stage of material glut has been achieved can the pendulum begin its move toward higher values and aspirations.
>
> PELLETIER, 1985

You might disagree with Farmer's views but in being part of a service that focuses on delivery to people the process can never be entirely scientific in nature. Nursing and midwifery are both science and art.

References

Allmark P and Klarzynski R (1992) The case against nurse advocacy, *British Journal of Nursing* 2(1): 33–36.

Allport G W (1954) *The Nature of Prejudice*. Massachusetts: Addison-Wesley.

Asch S (1955) Opinions and social pressure. *Scientific American* 193(5): 31–35.

Aspler R (1975) Effects of embarrassment on behaviour toward others. *Journal of Personality and Social Psychology* 32: 145–153.

Atkinson R L, Atkinson R C, Smith E E, Bem D J and Hilgard E R (1990) *Introduction to Psychology*, 10th edn. London: Harcourt Brace Jovanovich Inc.

Baron R A and Byrne D (1977) *Social Psychology: Understanding Human Interaction*. Boston: Allyn & Baker.

Bateson G, Jackson D, Haley J and Weakland J (1956) Towards a theory of schizophrenia. *Behavioural Science* 1: 251–264.

Bem D J (1967) Self-perception: An alternative interpretation of cognitive dissonance phenomena. *Psychological Review* 74: 183–200.

Booth T (1975) Growing up in Society. In: Herriot P (ed) *Essential Psychology*. London: Methuen and Co Ltd.

Cialdini RB et al (1975) Reciprocal concessions procedure for influencing compliance: The door in the face technique. *Journal of Personality and Social Psychology* 31: 206–215.

Congalton A A (1976) *The Individual in Society: An Introduction to Sociology for Nurses*. Chichester: John Wiley and Sons.

Durkheim E (1964) *The Rules of Sociological Method*. New York: Free Press.

Farmer B (1993) The use and abuse of power in nursing. *Nursing Standard* 7(23): 33–36.

Festinger L (1954) A theory of social comparison processes. *Human Relations* 7 117–140.

Festinger L (1957) *A Theory of Cognitive Dissonance*. California: Stanford University Press.

Freedman J L and Fraser S C (1966) Compliance without pressure: The foot in the door technique. *Journal of Personality and Social Psychology* 7: 117–124.

Heider F (1958) *The Psychology of Interpersonal Relations*. New York: John Wiley & Sons.

Katz D (1960) The functional approach to the measurement of attitudes. *Public Opinion Quarterly* 24: 163–204.

Kelman H C (1958) Compliance, identification and internalisation: Three processes of attitude change. *Journal of Conflict Resolution* 2: 51–60.

McGhie A (1973) *Psychology as Applied to Nursing*, 6th edn. London: Churchill Livingstone.

Milgram S (1963) Behavioural study of obedience. *Journal of Abnormal and Social Psychology* 67: 371–378.

Milgram S (1965) Some conditions of obediance and obediance to authority. *Human Relations* 18: 57–76.

Niven N (1989) *Health Psychology – An Introduction for Nurses and other Health Care Professionals*. London: Churchill Livingstone.

Open University (1986) *D102 Social Sciences: A Foundation Course. Block 8. Models of man and social science*. Milton Keynes: Open University Press.

Osgood C E and Tannenbaum P H (1955) The Principle of Congruity in the Prediction of Attitude Change. *Psychological Review* (62): 42–55.

Parsons T (1972) Definitions of health and illness in the light of American values and social structure. In: Jaco E G (ed) *Patients, Physicians and Illness: A Sourcebook in Behavioural Science and Health*. New York: Free Press.

Pellitier K R (1985) *Toward a Science of Consciousness*. California: Celestial Arts.

Pennington D C (1986) *Essential Social Psychology*. London: Edward Arnold.

Persell C H (1990) *Understanding Society – An Introduction to Sociology*, 3rd edn. London: Harper and Row.

Regan D T (1971) The effect of a favour and liking on compliance. *Journal of Experimental Social Psychology* 7: 627–639.

Sherif M (1936) *The Psychology of Social Norms*. New York: Harper & Row.

Skinner B F (1971) *Beyond Freedom and Dignity*. Harmondsworth: Penguin Books Ltd.

Spitz R A (1945) Hospitalism: An Inquiry into the Genesis of Psychiatric Conditions in Early Childhood. In: Bronfenbremner U (ed) *Influences on Human Development* (reprinted 1972). Illinois: Dryden Press.

Starr B D and Goldstein, HS (1975) *Human Development and Behaviour: Psychology in Nursing*. New York: Springer Publishing Company Inc.

Stuart G W and Sundeen S J (1979) *Principles and Practice of Psychiatric Nursing*. London: The C V Mosby Co.

United Kingdom Central Council (1992) *Code of Professional Conduct for the Nurse, Midwife and Health Visitor*, 3rd edn. London: UKCC.

Wallace J and Sadalla E (1966) Behavioural consequences of transgression: The effects of social recognition. *Journal of Experimental Research and Personality* 1: 187–194.

Yarrow M R, Schwartz C G, Murphy H S and Deasy L C (1955) The psychological meaning of mental illness in the family. *Journal of Social Issues* (11): 12–24.

CHAPTER 2

Divisions in Society

*. . . from my own experience of caring and
being cared for . . . more than anything
I have discovered that the world is not
divided into the sick and those who care for
them, but that we are all wounded and that
we all contain within our hearts that love
which is for the healing of nations. What we
lack is the courage to start giving it away.*

DR SHEILA CASSIDY (1988)

2 Divisions in Society

Introduction

This chapter builds on the information provided in Chapter 1 and addresses the following issues:

1 Class structure and sections within society

2 Life chances

3 Race

4 Gender

5 Inequalities in health

As with other chapters in this book, the ideas and activities that are presented in this chapter cannot, in such limited space, provide all the answers nor discuss all the permutations that exist in areas as complex as those listed above. What is provided is 'food for thought' and activities to stimulate thinking, and it is the hope of the authors that once completed, the chapter will have stimulated interest in finding out more from other sources.

Objectives

After reading through this chapter and undertaking the set activities you should be able to:

1 Demonstrate your awareness of those sociological factors which impinge on **health gain**.

2 Describe the ideologies of Adam Smith, Karl Marx and Max Weber and outline how each may have an impact on **health service provision**.

3 Identify how **life chances** influence both health and social standing.

4 Delineate between **biological** and **social/cultural** explanations of **sex/gender difference**.

5 Understand how **inequalities** in society influence health and well-being.

6 Understand more fully the role of the nurse/midwife in **promoting well-being and health gain**.

Studying Social Divisions

In Chapter 1 you briefly examined the concept of attitudes and their impact on personal behaviour. Chapter 2 asks you now to take forward that examination of personal attitudes and consider societal attitudes which influence divisions in our society. This consideration will prove of use as a foundation for the subsequent chapters of this text.

 Before addressing specific issues think about why it might be important for health professionals to study the concept of divisions in society. Make a note of your thoughts.

There are numerous reasons for studying societal divisions, but perhaps the most obvious one is the simple observation that not all members of society are the same. People vary in many ways, not just in their sex, colour or social class. Work, hobbies, income, living habitats, preferred mode of transport and beliefs, for instance, are all sources of difference which become important to our understanding of how society works – of how individuals 'fit in' to the scheme of life which exists in society. The distinctions and divisions that exist in a society enable individuals to be identified within that society to have a social identity. For example, when you first meet someone, among your initial questions are the following:

- '. . . and what do you do for a living?'
- 'Where do you live?'
- 'Which school did you go to?'

and so on . . .

Such questions begin to establish the parameters of an individual's social identity. When a client/patient is referred to health services similar questions are asked in order to establish a social picture of the person. People will also use other distinctions to identify individuals and groups in society, such as; 'she's rich', 'that family are snobs', 'those children go to a state school' (this labelling process will be explored more fully in Chapter 3). These distinctions are simple classifications used by people as indicators of similarity or difference between themselves and others.

 Further exploration of this idea can be found in: The Open University (1985) *Social Sciences – A Foundation Course. D102 Block 3: The Production of Social Divisions* – Units 10 & 11. Milton Keynes: the Open University Press.

As professional carers you will be involved with people from all walks of life, and you will need to be capable of applying your therapeutic skills equally to every client/patient in your care. The greater your understanding of social divisions, the greater the chance of breaking down some of the barriers that divisions create, and of counteracting the negative effects of such barriers on the individual.

Though the difference between societal divisions may be great – for example, the gulf between the wealthiest and the poorest people in the country – there exists as a general rule a relatively peaceful coexistence of these groups within society. This apparently peaceful coexistence has already been discussed at some depth in Chapter 1 and is largely due to the fact that as a member of society, each individual, irrespective of wealth, race or religion, or any other differentiating factor, experiences both choices and constraints. Each has some freedom of choice within their personal limitations. For instance, you may well have wanted to be a surgeon or maybe a psychiatrist, but due to certain constraints these careers were beyond your range of choices. So you chose a career in nursing or midwifery instead, thus reducing potential conflict and maintaining the coexistence of groups in society.

The first of these social divisions you will be examining in detail is that of class.

 *Nurses in particular have always been concerned with more than the medical care of their patients (or clients), and have perhaps felt or thought many of the things to which sociology gives articulation.*
JONES, R K & JONES, P A (1975) *Sociology in Medicine.*
London: English Universities Press.

Class Structure and Sections in Society

The class divisions of society provide possibly the most controversial and most fascinating aspect of all the social divisions. It is also the aspect that you may be most familiar with and have personally experienced, but how much do you know about the class structure of our society?

Think about the class structures apparent in our society and make notes on your awareness of the visible strata.

Although it is never safe to assume too much, it is imagined that you have noted such strata as 'upper class', 'middle class', 'working class' and 'lower class'.

You may also have included such issues as 'wealth distribution', 'social status', 'haves and have-nots', 'blue collar workers', 'white collar workers' and 'aristocracy'.

Similarly, some of you will have mentioned 'communism *vs* capitalism', 'working classes *vs* ruling classes' or 'bourgeoisie *vs* proletariat'.

Prominent people might well have entered your mind, including 'Karl Marx', 'Max Weber' or 'Adam Smith'. Whatever your present understanding of class structure, there is no denying that it serves to underpin the attitudes and prejudices of both individuals and groups in our society.

In order to put the current form of class structure into perspective it is necessary to take a brief look at history and travel back in time to late mediaeval Europe (*c.* 1100 to 1500).

Feudalism was the general system of social structure at this time and operated throughout Europe. It survived in many countries, including Japan and Russia, until the twentieth century, and still exists in some parts of Africa. The system was based, in theory, on an integration of rights and obligations. In its most fundamental form there were four social divisions (see Figure 2.1) and those of high status (the 'lords') had an obligation to protect those under them (the 'vassals'). The vassals had an obligation to serve the lord in war, to pay dues, to work for the lord and accept the judgement of the lord's court.

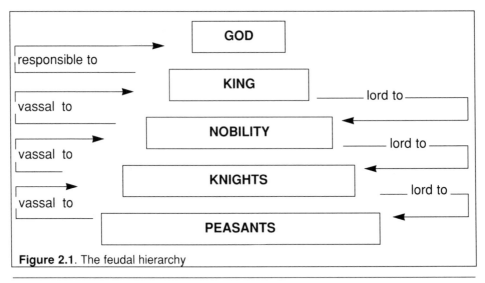

Figure 2.1. The feudal hierarchy

The king, nobility and knight divisions might have up to four grades, each with its own 'vassals' and 'lords'. For the 'serfs' there was a degree of social mobility. The serf could either enter the church as celibate clergy, which posed no threat to the nobility, or he could become a 'freeman' of the lord's estate, which meant he had to stay with the estate and keep free from punishable events for a year and a day (referred to as 'escape'). This upward mobility would not take the serf out of the peasant division but would elevate him within his own division.

The serfs used to earn income by exchanging their labour for money, generally by working on the estates of the lords. Indeed, the feudal system is often called the 'Estates System' and the king would charge his nobles to manage his estates. Each estate would have separate interpretations of the rights and obligations of, and their responsibilities to, each member of the social divisions according to the particular noble in charge.

Think about the above description of the feudal system and make notes on the following:

1 What are the similarities between this system and your current understanding of the contemporary class structure?

2 Why do you think the feudal system failed to survive in Western Europe?

Among the similarities will be the presence of different levels in the system, the notion of 'the haves' (king, nobles and knights) and the 'have-nots' (serfs) – each level having 'less' than the level above it. The serfs can possibly be identified with today's 'working class' – although many would not take kindly to the label 'serf'! The notion of social mobility, be it upward or downward, is one that has also survived the years. You will have noted the lack of reference to women within the feudal system, a reflection of the marked inequalities between men and women at that time. Today's gender divisions will be discussed later in the chapter.

The main reasons for the collapse of the feudal system were:

1 The power of the landed estate diminished as towns began to grow, and the population expanded. Individual lords could no longer enforce their own 'laws' within their estates.

2 Money began to circulate freely throughout the country as people became mobile in order to find work. People were no longer tied to one lord.

3 With the decline of the estates both political and legal affairs became centralised, and professional courts were established.

4 The notion of *'divine right'* was challenged.

5 The beginning of the Industrial Revolution.

The final collapse of the feudal system in Britain became the beginning of today's class structure. Social classes emerged where, in theory at least, there were no barriers to moving up (or down!) the social scale although then, as today, there were considerable practical barriers to social mobility.

 Before focusing on the ideologies and personalities which have influenced the growth of the class structure, reflect upon the feudal system as described and consider how the people may have been cared for, both during illness and while in good health.

Little is known with regard to health issues in mediaeval Europe, hence the way in which health was catered for can only be surmised. It may be safe to suggest that the king and his family would have received the attention of recognised 'men of science', while the peasants would have been cared for by their own families. It would be difficult to assess whether the king or the peasant received the most effective care given the practices of medical science prevailing at the time. It is known that the church frequently catered for the needs of the poorest people, and that the first British hospital, St Bartholomew's was founded in 1123, and nearly a century later the second, St Thomas' was founded in 1215.

The living conditions of the kings, nobles, knights and peasants would be comparable to their status, so the nobles, for example, would be less likely to suffer because of these conditions than would the peasants. It is difficult, though, to ascertain the true effects of these differences on the individuals. With regard to diet it is probably safe to assume that the peasants of feudal Europe did not have access to the same amounts or types of food as those of higher status. Whose diet was actually the healthiest is debatable.

Having mentioned some of the more feasible possibilities related to health care in feudal times, we would suggest that the higher your social status, the more attention and resources were available to you.

The class structure has been subject to many interpretations and it has inspired many personalities, each with their own ideological beliefs about the nature of class. We will now consider three of the main figures associated with the central theories of class structures and systems.

- Adam Smith (1723–1790)

- Karl Marx (1818–1883)

- Max Weber (1864–1920)

Adam Smith and the Self-Interested Individual

As life developed away from the traditional values and obligations of feudalism, the work of Adam Smith became influential in promoting the virtues of 'individual enterprise' in a 'free market system', and thus the capitalistic system of Britain produced its first champion. In its simplest terms, Smith's ideology promotes the belief that each individual has the freedom to pursue his or her own way of life, and that the state (government) only provides those things which individuals cannot, e.g. a legal system, public services (postal, transport, etc) and defence, all necessary to maintain the freedom of the individual's rights.

Smith hoped that if individuals followed their own interests, social harmony would ensue. On reflection, this may have been an over-optimistic view of human nature, but he also believed that the pursuit of 'self-interest' was not selfish as it would benefit family, friends, and other social contacts:

> *He will prevail if he can interest their love in his favour and show them it is for their own advantage to do for HIM what he requires of THEM. Give me that which I want and you shall have this which YOU want.*
>
> SMITH, 1970

In his book *The Wealth of Nations* (1970, first published in 1776), Smith argued that society is classified by its economic system and its rate of expansion. In order for individuals to enjoy 'free enterprise' he advocated that the state should not interfere in the country's economy.

Social mobility was believed by Smith to be the way in which individuals could improve their social status and this, coupled with free market competition, would produce equal opportunities for everyone willing to exploit the system. This is a remarkably similar ideology to that which became the cornerstone of 'Thatcherism' in the early 1980s and has been echoed in the words of other prominent politicians of the 1980s and 1990s. For instance those of Norman Tebbitt, 'get on your bike . . .' (emphasising the need to be mobile when seeking work opportunities in the United Kingdom) and John Major, '. . . the creation of a "classless" society . . .' (reference to the current government's policies on the economy and the public sector). This latter reference is similar in meaning to the one made in 1848 by J S Mill who believed that 'workers' should improve themselves '. . . *not by robbing capitalists, but by honestly acquiring capital for themselves*'. Thus all become capitalists (Open University, 1986).

Adam Smith was a man whose ideas on social issues still influence the modern world.

 Think about Adam Smith's ideology and make notes on how the health of the nation in the eighteenth century may have been influenced by his ideas.

Your answers to this activity will probably depend upon your opinion of Smith's beliefs, but the following suggestions may represent common responses.

1 The ultimate question posed by Smith's views is, 'Should health provision be provided by the state, or should individuals be responsible for their own health?'

  If you believe that 'health' should be provided by the state, is this because it is necessary for the 'protection of the individual's rights'? This would reflect the ideas of Smith, as indeed would the idea of health provision by an enterprising individual! Or are you of the opinion that health should be provided to everyone, as a collective right, irrespective of status within the system?

2 If you believe in Smith's doctrine of social order then you may suggest that health care should, where possible, be supplied by privately managed establishments, and the need for these would be dictated by 'market forces'. Only where the enterprising individual could not supply the demands of the market would the state make provision available, presumably in order to keep the workforce healthy and consequently sustain the economic system.

3 An alternative view is that those who could afford the care offered by enterprising individuals would receive the optimum heath care service, while those who could not would receive a second-rate service. The rationale of this is that the best carers would be working for those enterprising individuals, where the rewards for their skills would, arguably, be greater. Current criticisms of the advent of Directly Managed Units (DMUs) and Trusts within the National Health Service include the forecast that they will create such a two-tier service, leading to inequality of provision for patients/clients.

4 If you believe that there should be health provision for everyone, irrespective of social status or wealth, then the social order of Smith is not one you would advocate. Smith's ideas, which he believed would create equality, could in fact result in a great divide between those who could afford 'the best' and those who could not. As an advocate of a 'system of equality', you would view the option of all people having equal access to the same facilities, as being paramount.

You will have realised that many of the arguments raised by Adam Smith's ideology are still in evidence today. The section on 'Inequalities in Health' later in this chapter addresses further the influence of Smith's ideology on latter day health issues.

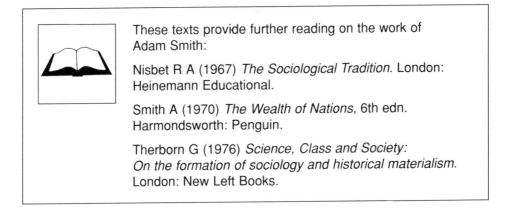

These texts provide further reading on the work of Adam Smith:

Nisbet R A (1967) *The Sociological Tradition*. London: Heinemann Educational.

Smith A (1970) *The Wealth of Nations*, 6th edn. Harmondsworth: Penguin.

Therborn G (1976) *Science, Class and Society: On the formation of sociology and historical materialism.* London: New Left Books.

Karl Marx – Communities, Constraints and Social Conflicts

The ideology of Karl Marx and his colleague, Friedrich Engels, was in direct conflict with that of Smith. Marx viewed self-interest as a selfish product of a capitalist society and his ideas were developed to provide an alternative to capitalism, based on the needs of communities (the people collectively) and not on the needs (selfishness?) of individuals.

Marx despised the notion of 'self-interest' and the competition this resulted in, and he developed his ideas as an ideology of change –

Philosophers have interpreted the world, the point however is to change it . . .

MARX, 1888

Marx was active at a time of great change throughout Europe; during the 1840s he travelled from his native Germany to France and eventually to Britain, and witnessed the political and economic strife of working people. From these observations Marx concluded that the capitalist system, far from being beneficial to family, friends and the individual, actually isolated the working people by reducing their value within society to nothing more than an expendable commodity. To Marx, the workers and the labour they provided were, in a capitalist system, little more than a means to an end for the manufacturers (capitalists) and were another 'object' in the production process, thus individuals became tied to the needs of the manufacturer and not themselves. This not only dehumanised the working people, but also demoralised the largest section of society – the 'working classes'.

Whereas 'individualism' was seen by Adam Smith as being the most important aspect of social identity, Marx on the other hand viewed 'Groups and Communities' as being the main means of identification within society. Marxist philosophy emphasised the experiences that the people of differing social groups shared with each other; in other words Marx felt that society was divided into groups united by common interests. This would suggest that Marx did not see social divisions simply as 'the rich', 'the poor' and 'those in the middle'. He also considered occupation to be an important element in determining membership of different social groups, so that a soldier, a mechanic and a nurse might earn similar salaries but would not belong to the same social 'class'. Marx, unlike Smith, believed that as the industries of nations developed, the workers would unite once they recognised their class interests and revolution against capitalism would ensue. From this a society of equals would be developed. It was from these principles that the 'bourgeoisie' (the capitalists) and 'proletariat' (the workers) entered into the debate on class structure (see Figure 2.2).

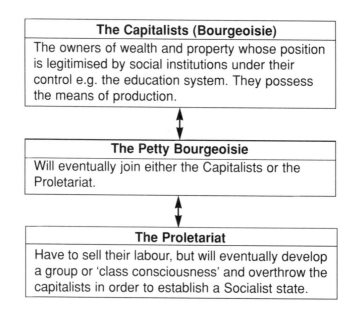

| **The Capitalists (Bourgeoisie)** |
| The owners of wealth and property whose position is legitimised by social institutions under their control e.g. the education system. They possess the means of production. |

| **The Petty Bourgeoisie** |
| Will eventually join either the Capitalists or the Proletariat. |

| **The Proletariat** |
| Have to sell their labour, but will eventually develop a group or 'class consciousness' and overthrow the capitalists in order to establish a Socialist state. |

Figure 2.2. The Marxist class system.

It can be seen from this diagram that Marx believed that the system, which is controlled by the bourgeoisie, was designed to perpetuate the divide between the social classes. History has shown that the 'Marxist Revolution' has not been fully achieved, but the philosophy of Marx, like that of Adam Smith, still has a profound influence on the observations made, and the attitudes held, by people on divisions in society today.

 Think about the Marxist vision of society, and make notes on how the health of the nation may have been influenced by this ideology.

THE INDIVIDUAL IN SOCIETY

The first question posed by Marxism is, 'Can there be equality in health provision?' There is no simple answer to this. The provision of services for ill people, people with a handicap, people with a disability, people with mental health disorders and other minority or disadvantaged individuals would have to be provided at the same level of service enjoyed by the majority of the population. Is this feasible? Do you know of any societies or countries that seek to achieve this balance?

Marxists would view the National Health Service (NHS) as one of the state-run institutions which 'legitimise' class differences. The reason would be that the NHS was initiated by the 'ruling classes' in order to keep the workforce healthier (not wealthier) and thus ensure that the proletariat could provide the bourgeoisie with more labour, therefore more wealth.

However, it could be argued that the NHS has provided a greater degree of health equality by making opportunity for health gain widely accessible to the general population. The NHS, since its beginning in 1948, has also provided increasingly specialised care for many people from minority and disadvantaged groups, thus helping to ensure parity between societal groups.

Conversely, it could be argued that the 'special' services have only alienated the people who use them from the general population, so that equality cannot and does not exist. In fact these services may deny the users an identity within the general population by reinforcing their belonging to a minority or disadvantaged group.

Within the United Kingdom there exist two main options for health care – one is the NHS, the other is private health care schemes. The former is largely 'free at source' (although we all pay for it indirectly through personal contributions and taxation), the latter are paid for by those willing and able to pay directly. As you are probably aware, there are numerous political and economic debates concerning the pros and cons of the two health-care systems. Applying the basic principles of Marxism and Capitalism to these debates provides some interesting areas of argument around self-interest of individuals and their health versus health for all.

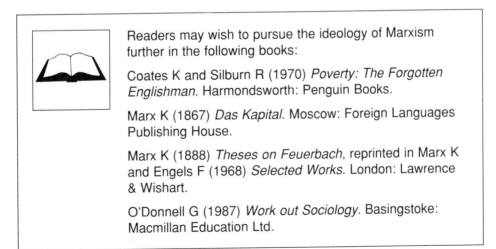

Readers may wish to pursue the ideology of Marxism further in the following books:

Coates K and Silburn R (1970) *Poverty: The Forgotten Englishman.* Harmondsworth: Penguin Books.

Marx K (1867) *Das Kapital.* Moscow: Foreign Languages Publishing House.

Marx K (1888) *Theses on Feuerbach*, reprinted in Marx K and Engels F (1968) *Selected Works.* London: Lawrence & Wishart.

O'Donnell G (1987) *Work out Sociology.* Basingstoke: Macmillan Education Ltd.

Max Weber – Class and the Notion of Life Chances

At the time when Weber developed his social theories in the early part of the twentieth century, it was apparent that the class distinctions between the capitalist bourgeoisie and the workers of the proletariat had in fact, contrary to Marx's predictions, widened and not disappeared. Not only had the division between these groups grown, but the groups themselves also appeared to have subdivided. It was Weber's observations and theories on these social developments which have provided many of the criteria used today to determine an individual's social class.

Similarly to Smith, Weber believed in the rights of the 'individual', but he also recognised that the individual was dominated by the organisations which controlled not only the economic forces of a country, but also other social and cultural influences, for example religion and politics. (The influence of societal institutions is addressed further in Chapter 4.) These organisations, according to Weber, legitimised their own position in the social order. This was similar to the ideas of Marx. Weber tried to integrate the links between all these factors to identify a person's class and social position. The important distinctions which Weber identified were:

1 **Class** – determined by *income* and *wealth*. Also how these affected the opportunity of gaining other valued possessions, especially *property* and *services*.

2 **Status** – the unequal distribution of styles of life and the consumption of commodities. Status is linked closely to class, particularly class derived from *occupation*.

3 **Power** or **Parties** – the individual's ability to influence the actions of others, for example via political parties, trade unions, professional associations.

Weber's theories acknowledged that society was largely dominated by a system of capitalism, as advocated by industrial barons, and by the undeniable influence of state bureaucracy, which in Weber's case was exercised by the state of Prussia (Germany). Weber found himself admitting that bureaucracy was an efficient system, yet he also warned that a bureaucratic state could further the interests of those who run the state at the expense of others within it, thus perpetuating, once again, the divisions in society. Weber also pursued the notions and values of bureaucracy during the course of his work, but it is his analysis of class divisions which provides contemporary sociologists with a model for class position. The Registrar General's classification is widely used to express class differences in a hierarchical manner (see Figure 2.3).

In more recent times numerous attempts have been made to update Weber's theories on class, and this has often resulted in each of the 'classes' being sub-divided or re-defined. The Hall Jones scale, for instance, which was devised in the 1950s, splits Social Class 3 into three separate areas (see Jones and Jones, 1975 p.70), while Halsey (1980) divides the classes into three areas (service, intermediate, working), but sub-divides these into eight divisions. It is also worth noting that many of these scales are based upon the occupation,

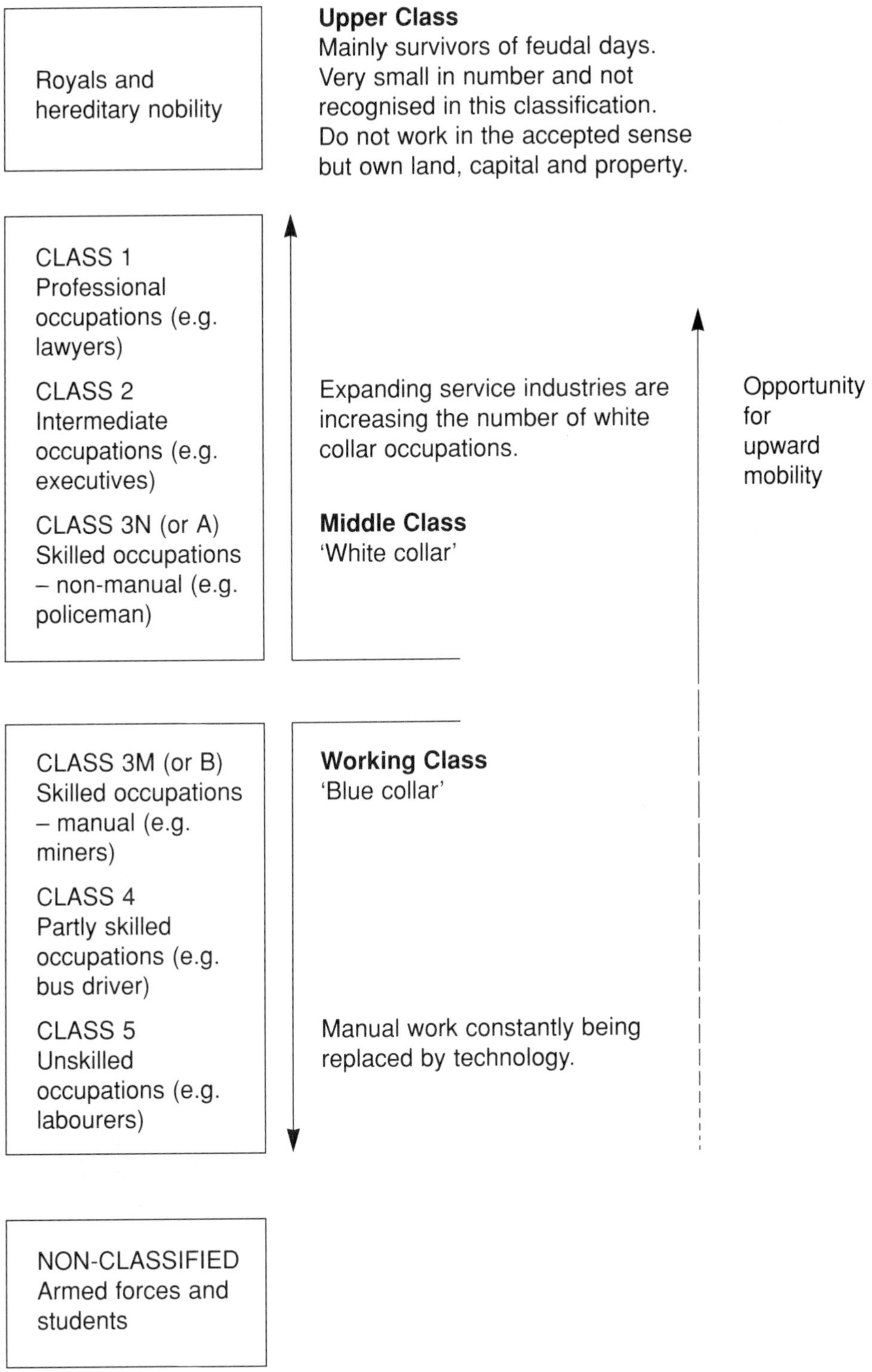

Royals and hereditary nobility	**Upper Class** Mainly survivors of feudal days. Very small in number and not recognised in this classification. Do not work in the accepted sense but own land, capital and property.

CLASS 1 Professional occupations (e.g. lawyers) CLASS 2 Intermediate occupations (e.g. executives) CLASS 3N (or A) Skilled occupations – non-manual (e.g. policeman)	Expanding service industries are increasing the number of white collar occupations. **Middle Class** 'White collar'	Opportunity for upward mobility
CLASS 3M (or B) Skilled occupations – manual (e.g. miners) CLASS 4 Partly skilled occupations (e.g. bus driver) CLASS 5 Unskilled occupations (e.g. labourers)	**Working Class** 'Blue collar' Manual work constantly being replaced by technology.	

NON-CLASSIFIED
Armed forces and students

Figure 2.3. Registrar General's classification

property, and income of the so-called 'head of household' – this person having traditionally been a male. Perhaps with the growth of sex and gender equalities future scales will, rightly, reflect the status of females within society.

It is rare to find two scales which entirely agree. For example, nursing is generally accepted to be a middle-class occupation, but depending on which scale is used may fall into either Class 1, Class 2 or Class 3.

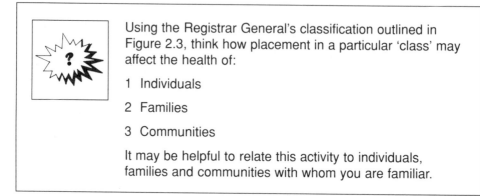

Using the Registrar General's classification outlined in Figure 2.3, think how placement in a particular 'class' may affect the health of:

1 Individuals

2 Families

3 Communities

It may be helpful to relate this activity to individuals, families and communities with whom you are familiar.

In order to complete the activity you have to assume that class impinges on health; that health gains are variable for different classes in society. Research does demonstrate a link between health issues and class status:

The lack of improvement, and in some respects deterioration of the health experiences of the unskilled and semi-skilled manual classes (5 and 4) relative to Class 1, throughout the 1960s and early 1970s is striking.

THE BLACK REPORT, 1980

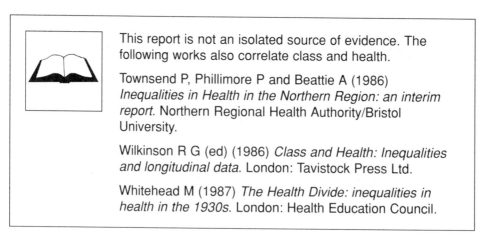

This report is not an isolated source of evidence. The following works also correlate class and health.

Townsend P, Phillimore P and Beattie A (1986) *Inequalities in Health in the Northern Region: an interim report.* Northern Regional Health Authority/Bristol University.

Wilkinson R G (ed) (1986) *Class and Health: Inequalities and longitudinal data.* London: Tavistock Press Ltd.

Whitehead M (1987) *The Health Divide: inequalities in health in the 1930s.* London: Health Education Council.

What these latter reports identified was that the 'health divide' had in fact grown wider since the publication of The Black Report in 1980. They will be returned to in the section on 'inequalities'. For the current activity it can be noted that a person's class status may well be a determinant of their health.

But how? Perhaps one of the most significant issues is the life-style of families from the various social classes. Health is not merely the result of an individual's physical well-being, but also includes social, psychological, spiritual, and environmental well-being. People in Class 1, for instance, may well be in a better position to fulfil their environmental needs than people in Class 5. Wealth and income are important considerations in meeting those needs, especially in terms of purchasing healthy food, clothing, home improvements, prescriptions and access to health care. In fact, financial outlay is correlated strongly with individual and community life-styles and cost is a factor in effectively promoting holistic well-being. It is a sobering thought that the Black Report suggested that a child born within a family of Class 5 status, was *twice* as likely to die before the age of one year than a child born to parents with professional occupations.

Poverty, individual motivation, lack of opportunities for social mobility, lowered social expectations, lack of access to health provision and to education are all factors influencing health and are in turn directly related to the class divide, but arguably the two most significant factors are wealth and income.

Recognising these social influences on health leads one to realise that 'health for all' is not merely a matter of having a National Health Service, excellence in medical technology or research-based nursing practice. 'Health for all' requires change at a societal level not just within the 'health' community.

Life Chances

'Life Chances' are, according to Weber, those opportunities which present themselves to individuals in society. Weber believed the ability to gain access to life chances was the single most important element in an individual's life determining their social class. But not only is access to life chances important, so too is the willingness of the individual to take those chances. In later years the term 'social mobility' became synonymous with movement both up and down the social scale. Social mobility can occur only if individuals take advantage of the opportunities presented to them – in other words their 'life chances'.

 Think about your own life, and reflect upon Weber's notion of 'life chances'. Make notes on what you think your life chances have been and what chances may present themselves in the future?

Life chances may occur at any stage of individual development but there are general opportunities which apply to almost everyone:

Education – this does not necessarily mean the type of school attended, but more the opportunities taken by individuals while at school. These may include the more obvious opportunities such as learning experiences in the classroom plus the acquisition of qualifications and the less obvious such as outings, recreation and relationship formation.

Occupation – this includes making progress within the organisation. Individuals can use the opportunities provided by their occupation to gain access to other life chances. These may be financial, recreational or relational, for example.

Wealth – irrespective of the individual's income, the manner in which people use their wealth can provide them with many other life chances, e.g. leisure and recreation, housing, possessions.

Many opportunities are created by the individuals themselves, some are presented by other people. Occasionally chances develop accidentally, and it is up to the individual to utilise and exploit these life chances to their fullest potential. (How often have you said, 'If only I'd listened to . . .', or 'I wonder what would have happened if I had . . .'?)

Social mobility is often seen as being facilitated through one's occupation. However, occupations are frequently determined by abilities, experiences, qualifications and so on – that is, by attributes concomitant to life chances. Therefore, life chances via occupation influence social mobility and vice versa. Life chances engender progress and in turn progression opens up further life chances. On the other hand, restricted life chances hinder progress within an ever-increasing downward spiral.

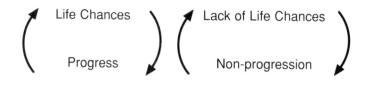

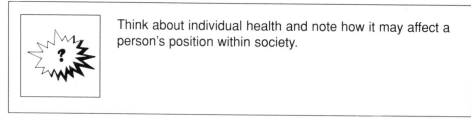

Think about individual health and note how it may affect a person's position within society.

There is evidence to suggest that 'social selection' i.e. the influence of health on individuals' social mobility, and consequently their social position, is a major contributory factor to social differences in health (Blane et al, 1993). The Black Report also suggested that social selection is one of four processes which may be responsible for creating social differences, particularly in relation to health. The person who is healthy has greater opportunity to move up the social scale than someone who is unhealthy.

One common example of this process at work is the disadvantage and discrimination faced by disabled people who, despite being supported by legislation such as the Disabled Persons (Employment) Act 1944, still find

THE INDIVIDUAL IN SOCIETY

difficulty in finding suitable employment (Blaxter, 1976). The irony faced by the majority of disabled people is that they are not 'ill' in the everyday sense of the word, and it is the effects of the label 'disabled' which frequently produce the negative associations. (There is greater discussion of this labelling process in Chapter 3.) Another example of health affecting social mobility is the promotion prospects of those who become seriously ill. Here the evidence points strongly to prejudice being demonstrated against employees who are eligible for promotion, if they have suffered an illness in their past. Illsley (1986) provided a strong case for illness being a primary factor in 'downward' social mobility. Unfortunately statistics on the relationship between class and health may suffer from distortion, for example people who are in poor health, but still capable of work, may opt for unemployment and consequently would not figure in studies of upward or downward social mobility based on occupational categories (Blane et al., 1993).

Invariably, downward mobility reduces the income as well as the status of the person concerned and, as you discovered earlier, lowering of status can result in psychological, social and spiritual suffering. These, allied to the original health problem, can leave the individual, plus family, requiring support in order for them to cope with their new orientation to life. It is important that care professionals understand as much as possible about people's circumstances and their holistic needs. Holistic care relies on holistic assessment, which identifies social determinants as important factors to consider when attempting to achieve health gain.

Blane D, Davey Smith G and Bartley M (1993) Social selection; what does it contribute to social class differences in health? *Sociology of Health and Illness,* **15**(1): 1–15.

Blaxter M (1976) *The Meaning of Disability: a sociological study of impairment*, London: Heinemann Educational.

Illsley R (1986) Occupational class, selection, and the production of inequalities, *Quarterly Journal of Social Affairs* **2**: 151–161.

Race
To exclude consideration of race from this chapter would be to deny that racial divisions exist within our society. As nurses and midwives you will care for patients/clients who are of different racial origin from your own and such care must be delivered without prejudice or discrimination. (Chapter 3 examines prejudice and discrimination in the caring professions in greater depth.) It is hoped that in completing this section you will develop an understanding of racial issues which can be utilised to enhance your effectiveness as a practitioner and as a member of society. Before exploring specific racial issues here is a short activity to examine your attitudes towards race.

Think about 'race' and make a note of what comes to mind.

Responses will depend on life experiences and probably your own ethnic background. However, common replies include:

Race = 'people of different ethnic origins'

'descendants who share common ancestors'

'people from different countries'

You may have mentioned such issues as 'racism' 'racial equality' 'racial discrimination' 'race riots' 'apartheid' 'positive discrimination'. You may have also included a list of different nationalities 'Chinese' 'Indian' 'Pakistani' 'British' – and those of you who think more laterally may have added 'French' 'Italian' 'German' 'Japanese' and so on! Finally, you may have mentioned globally used categorisations such as 'Caucasian', 'Asian', 'African', 'Afro-Caribbean' and 'Arab'. This variety of possible responses indicates that 'race' is not merely a question of 'black' or 'white' in terms both of complexity and of skin colour.

Some readers may have noted the numerous 'labels' that are attached to people from different racial origins, many of which are derogative in nature. Terms such as 'black' and 'coloured' are widely used but often carry negative expectations along with the 'label'. (This process is examined further in Chapter 3.)

Racial awareness is a very personal concept, as is the application of prejudice. However, the existence of racial prejudice within a probably multicultural team of professionals delivering services to a multicultural set of consumers can only hinder the effectiveness of care given. (This potential conflict between personal and professional values is addressed in the latter part of Chapter 3.) This section now concentrates on the sociological aspects of race.

Many countries are composed of multiracial and multicultural communities, and both the health and social services provided by these countries must be able to respond to the health and social needs of this population. The nurse's/midwife's role in caring within multiracial societies will be enhanced by awareness of social divisions that may affect the well-being of ethnic groups. But why do such divisions occur? Numerous reasons have been given; what follows are the three most prevalent explanations.

The Biological Explanation

This explanation indicates that **physical** differences, such as hair and skin colour, are the reason for racial divisions. The assumption of this theory is that there are pre-determined differences between races, i.e. genetically pre-determined variances. These differences relate not only to colour but also to intelligence, cultural development and civilisation. It was this explanation which Adolf Hitler adopted in the 1930s to promote the 'genetically superior' Aryan race, and later in the 1960s it was used to justify the South African apartheid system. The promotion of the 'genetically superior' race led the Nazis to condemn over three million 'genetically inferior' people to death before the end of the Second World War in 1945. It was the strength of the Eugenics Movement's commitment to a 'superior gene pool' which contributed to the segregation of the male and female inhabitants of the Victorian asylums. The 'inferior gene pool' of the asylum inhabitants would not be able to reproduce and thus its eradication would be ensured. These abuses of the biological explanation have their impact on modern society in the context of the strong controversy surrounding the use of genetic engineering.

 Think about 'racial types' and attempt to classify the different races according to the biological distinctions between them.

This may have been a relatively straightforward activity. After all, there are some obvious differences which can be noted – e.g. skin colour, hair colour and style, and stature. But once these differences were noted did you struggle to continue the list? When classifying human beings, the western, and therefore mainly 'white', socio-anthropologists have divided humans into three groups:

1 *Negroid* – comprising mainly of people of African descent.

2 *Mongoloid* – comprising mainly of people of Eastern Asian descent.

3 *Caucasoid* – comprising mainly of people of European descent.

Classifications on their own say very little. Even a person's skin colour is not easy to classify, e.g. the caucasoid (white) group has within it people of dark skin, such as groups from Northern India and Australian Aborigines. What of the intra-group differences? Are there not tall and short people in each group? Within the European races do not some people have fair hair, dark hair and red hair? There are Scandinavians with dark hair and dark skin, and blond Aborigines. In fact the list of physical inter-group differences is far longer than the list of similarities. Conversely the similarities between people in the differently classified groups outweigh the differences.

Also worth noting is that centuries of human migration and mixing has further diluted the so-called biological differences between the races of the world. If there are so many similarities between the races why do social divisions still exist? In Victorian Britain the assumption was made that people of other races (i.e. non-white) lacked intelligence – intelligence being a pre-requisite of social functioning. This Victorian reasoning served to justify why colonisation was essential; to bring 'civilisation' to 'uncivilised' countries. Africa was seen as 'backward' compared to Britain, which was 'civilised', and this assumption was soon linked with the physical differences. There are many arguments about racial intelligence, but there is no conclusive proof to suggest that intellect is solely determined by racial origin, and therefore by biologically inherited differences. Intelligence is dependent on numerous factors, among which are 'life chances' and the opportunities provided by them, social environments and cultural beliefs. Minority racial groups are by and large disadvantaged within any society and may have constantly to prove themselves to be intellectually equal to those people in the majority. The stereotyping of many minority racial groups in society further hinders this process of equality (see Chapter 3).

Further information is provided in:

Open University (1985) *D102. Social Sciences – A Foundation Course. Block 3. The Production of Social Divisions. Unit 11.* pp. 59–66. Milton Keynes: Open University Press.

The Social Explanation – A Weberian Perspective

This perspective considers social circumstances to be the main reason for the creation of racial divisions, the initial divisions being a direct result of racial discrimination between different groups. This leads to competition for resources including education, housing, employment and ultimately social status. Thus each racial group will, while competing for these resources, grow further away from each other, reinforcing the social and racial divisions between them. This explanation for racial divisions relies on racial groups discriminating against each other. That is, giving preference to a person based on their social or physical attributes, instead of preference based on merit or abilities. Does this 'group competition' theory totally explain the racial divisions in society?

Think about the group competition theory outlined above and make notes on its manifestation in contemporary society.

Discrimination can be found in all aspects of life, but perhaps the most conspicuous examples are to be found in the employment and labour market. Between 1972 and 1975 the Political and Economic Planning group (PEP) conducted a major survey on racial disadvantage, and the evidence suggested that the black population were overrepresented in the lower paid and unskilled occupations and conversely were underrepresented at the other end of the occupational scale. The PEP survey also demonstrated that, proportionately, black workers experienced unemployment more than their white counterparts. Figure 2.4 is a graphic representation of the findings.

Housing was identified as another area where discrimination occurred, this being particularly noticeable in poorly conditioned rented accommodation, where the black population were again overrepresented. The Black Report (1980) suggests that poor housing is one of the factors contributing to the inequalities in health faced by many ethnic groups.

Discrimination in educational opportunities also illustrates group competition. Numerous studies have shown that there is a link between social class and education. For example, middle-class children are advantaged by having wider access to books at home and greater parental expectations. Jackson and Marsden (1962) and Hargreaves et al. (1975) provide excellent introductions to the education debate. However, perhaps the greatest source of discrimination is provided by teachers themselves. O'Donnell (1987) outlines how the Rampton Report (HMSO, 1981) pointed to black children being disadvantaged by racism, language problems, inappropriate curricula and poor relationships with teachers. Speculation on the underlying reason for this situation focuses on the fact the vast majority of teachers are themselves middle-class and that they therefore find it easier to relate to their own class group. Support is given to this point by the report suggesting that white working-class children suffer the same discrimination.

If, as you discovered earlier, life chances are created through occupation, wealth and education then you may feel that Weberian theory is a credible explanation for racial divisions. But explanation also needs to be given as to why groups compete for resources and why inequality is associated with such competition. Weber suggests that inequalities arise because groups struggle to maximise their own rewards at the expense of others, effectively reducing the rewards of the 'losing' group. In order to create the maximum chance of 'winning' a group will utilise any social or physical characteristic of the opposing group as a means to gain 'a competitive edge'. Common examples of this process include the use of *religion* in N. Ireland, the use of *language* in Wales and Scotland and, as we have seen in most countries with a multicultural society, the use of racial differences.

This theory relies on people believing in racial stereotypes and the potential threat that they represent. The competition element transcends the traditional class divisions according to Weberian scholars but by itself does not provide all the answers. While it is accepted that competition between groups does exist, it is also noteworthy that competition within groups will exist too, especially if the rewards are sufficiently motivating.

The Alternative Social Explanation – A Marxist Perspective

This perspective is based on the Marxist concepts of capitalism and class which have little to do with race; the Marxist explanations of class division give little

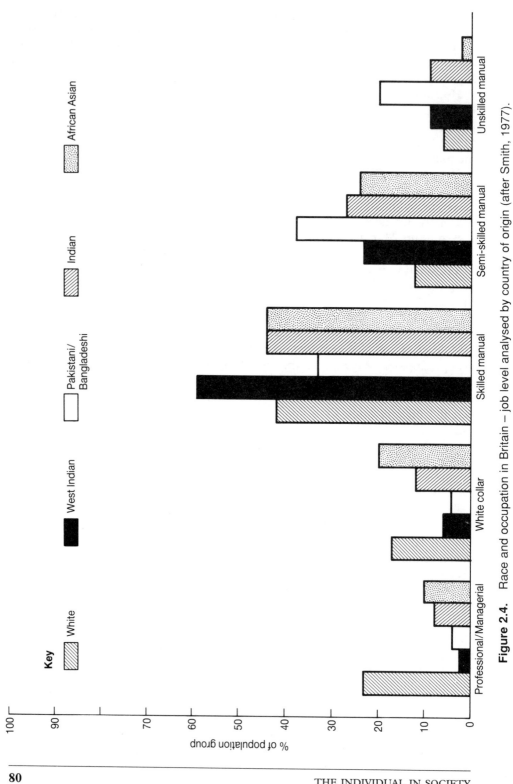

Figure 2.4. Race and occupation in Britain – job level analysed by country of origin (after Smith, 1977).

importance to the colour of a person's skin. However, Marxist theorists have attempted to incorporate racial division within a class framework. According to Marxist theory, racial divisions have occurred because of the historical exploitation of people from the colonies for economic profit. This is best illustrated in Britain by the experience of the migrant workforce of the 1950s and 1960s, which was exploited to provide labour.

 Think about this Marxist explanation for racial division. Make notes on how class may influence the development of such racial divisions.

The prime argument for class being influential in creating racial divisions lies in the need for production, and the criterion that in order to sustain production at acceptable costs it is necessary for the capitalist to employ labour at the most profitable rate available. Traditionally this labour had been provided by workers from within the country itself, but the years following the Second World War left the capitalist economies of the West with a dearth of labour, especially in the unskilled and semi-skilled sectors. Many workers from the home labour force had found employment in the newly created service sectors, developing their skills in the process and thus depleting still further the ranks of unskilled and semi-skilled workers.

Marxist theory now assumes that Western capitalists were faced with three options:

1 Raise wages in the manual sector to attract the home labour back.

2 Attract workers from poorer countries, especially in Europe.

3 Capitalist countries who had colonies could turn to the workers from these countries.

For Britain it was Poland which, immediately after the war, supplied large influxes of labour. Later, in 1948, it was immigrants from the West Indies, and in the 1950s immigrants from India and Pakistan were being encouraged into the labour market. This was a time of great production in Britain, and the migrant labour was gratefully received by the capitalists who employed them. But when recession began to hit production, particularly in manufacturing where most immigrants were employed, immigration controls were imposed which reduced the number of immigrants Britain would admit. This action was not opposed by the employers, who were then accused of exploiting workers within the capitalist system. That is, the employment (exploitation) of cheap labour assisted in producing profits, but when the market collapsed, as it did in the recession, this labour was no longer required and restrictions were then placed on the labour force (Immigration Laws).

Theorists would argue that the migrant workers were utilised by the capitalists at the expense of home labour, thus creating the beginnings of racial divisions. This was compounded by the low pay received by immigrant workers which undermined the position, and hence wages, of British workers. This impact on wages did nothing to harmonise group relations and ultimately led to division based on racial grounds. These arguments are the bases of Marxist theories on the racial divide in Britain.

Further information may be found in:
Open University (1985) *D102. Social Sciences – A Foundation Course. Block 3: The Production of Social Divisions*, Unit 11, pp. 75–83. Milton Keynes: Open University Press.

Two Manifestations of Racism

In generalised terms there are two types of racism present in society. There is *personal* racism and *institutional* racism. The former of these may be utilised by all individuals irrespective of their origins, while the latter is less overt and controlled by relatively small numbers of individuals.

Personal Racism

Think about the term 'personal racism' and make notes on what this means to you.

Each reader is likely to have a differing interpretation of 'personal racism'. This is logical simply because you are identifying 'personal' issues, and these interpretations are based upon your own experiences, influences, prejudices and so on. Personal racism is a relatively overt manifestation of racism, and is generally expressed in such activities as:

Verbal abuse

Physical abuse

Open discrimination

THE INDIVIDUAL IN SOCIETY

Institutional Racism

Now reflect on the term 'institutional racism' and make notes on your interpretation of this term.

Many readers may have experienced institutional racism without realising it. This type of racism is generally more covert and very damaging to the people against whom it discriminates. Unlike personal racism, which tends to be individualised and largely unorganised (though racial extremists may become organised groups), institutional racism is exercised in an organised and deliberate way by the institutions which form the infrastructure of society. Many organisations perpetrate institutional racism, which is manifested in various ways; for example:

Denial of employment opportunities

Restricted lending policies

Delay in processing benefits

Unfortunately, racism can manifest itself in all walks of life, and the caring sector is not immune from its effects. A heightened awareness of racism will better prepare you to counter the negative aspects of both personal and institutional racism.

Brown C (1984) *Black and White*, Policy Studies Institute. London: Heinemann Education.

Haralambos M (1985) *Sociology, New Directions*. Ormskirk: Causeway Press Limited.

McNaught A (1988) *Race and Health Policy*. New York: Croom Helm.

To conclude this section on racial division, read the following quotation and complete the activity which follows it:

Research has shown that attitudes towards coloured people are determined mainly by contact with attitudes rather than with the coloured people themselves. If we are surrounded by prejudiced people we are more likely to adopt their attitudes through simple contact over time.

JONES AND JONES, 1975

Think about what you have learnt in this section and reflect upon the above quotation.

The above quotation indicates that many individuals do not always use their own perceptions and knowledge of racial issues to make decisions regarding the people affected by such issues. As nurses and midwives you must be aware of the influence of the attitudes of professional colleagues and those of your patients/clients and act where necessary to avoid conforming to prejudicial or discriminatory practices. (Further guidance on this is contained in Chapter 3.)

In addition, understanding why racial divisions occur, as well as how they do, provides direction for meaningful intervention.

Gender

There are many similarities between the disadvantages stemming from racial divisions and the disadvantages created by gender differences. These will be explored shortly, but first a brief activity to determine the nature of 'gender'.

'Gender' has become common terminology, particularly in recent years. What does the word mean to you? Brainstorm and list ideas and issues that seem to you to be characteristic of gender considerations.

Gender is usually defined in terms of sex; its presence (in the context of the two sexes) or its absence (in terms of sexlessness). It relates to a classification of the sexes in terms of male or female.

What do these definitions tell you? In truth, very little except that gender is something to do with males and females, and a means of classifying male/female 'things'! The real point of this activity is to demonstrate that 'gender' has come to mean different things to different people and you may find it useful to compare your ideas with those of colleagues, particularly those of the opposite sex. With the advent of women's rights and feminism (a movement against the gender inequalities in society), especially in the Western world, gender has become focused on the roles and behaviour of the sexes – that is, on being masculine or feminine. Such roles and their associated behaviour are, as you discovered in the opening section to this chapter, governed by societal expectations. The traditional expectations attached to gender roles have been challenged by the feminist movement in particular and therefore gender divisions will be addressed with specific reference to the experiences of women in our society.

However, consideration will be given first to the theories which have been put forward to explain 'the sex differences' between males and females. There are two main theories offering explanation:

1 The *biological* explanation.

2 The *social and cultural* explanation.

The Biological Explanation

 When talking of the sexes, many people refer to the 'opposite sex'. Think about this term and identify what is meant by 'opposite', using biological factors/characteristics as your reference point.

There are no authors' suggestions on this activity, but without doubt you will have thought about differences and physical characteristics. Keep your notes ready for comparison with the reasons now put forward to explain biological differences.

The exponents of the biological theory believe that the 'opposites' found between the sexes are natural, and therefore the roles and behaviour acquired in life are a biological destiny. It is interesting to note that the leading exponents of this theory are male (see Morris, 1967, Tiger, 1969). In basic terms the biological explanation is as follows:

- The biological structures of men and women are 'designed' to fulfil the biological roles and behaviour of their particular sex.

- Male role behaviour is said to include aggressiveness, independence, logical thought, emotional stability, dominance, toughness, ruthlessness and ambition.

- Female role behaviour is described as passive, caring, non-violent, timid, emotional, nurturing.

The believers of biological theory argue that social roles are closely correlated with the biological roles of men and women. As the main biological function of women is identified as child-rearing and that of men as protecting and providing for the woman during her pregnancy, women are biologically structured to 'love and care', while men are structured to 'hunt and protect' (*see* Open University, 1985). Thus this theory reduces the social differences that exist between the sexes to a simple matter of biology. But this explanation has several weaknesses. It may be a relatively straightforward exercise to list physical differences and to a lesser extent the commonly ascribed behaviours of each sex. However, there is a degree of difficulty in explaining why some men, for instance, wish to stay at home with their children, or why women become successful business people.

 The biological explanation of the male/female divide is one that many people, especially men, believe to be 'natural'. There are many valid arguments against this proposition. Can you think of any?

Perhaps the most significant argument lies in the way humans learn to behave, and the methods by which behaviour is reinforced. Without question, there are biological differences between the sexes – for example, physiological, genetic, and hormonal – but these alone do not explain the behaviour of each sex. Behaviour is additionally determined by the social and cultural environment in which we live. If behaviour were solely biologically determined there would be no need for humans to adapt to their differing environments.

Dissenters point out that the main research in this biological arena has been predominantly based in Western societies and in this context the 'evidence', generally presented by males, appears to lean towards the 'biological'. But work carried out in other parts of the world, particularly among the tribal communities of South America, suggests that men and women are capable of behaving in similar fashion and in some cases women can and will be the dominant sex in a relationship. If it were 'natural' for man to be the hunter and woman the home-maker, surely all communities would reflect this tendency.

One last argument against the biological explanation of gender divisions has a historical basis and parallels the experience of migrant workers in post-war Britain. When society and the policy-makers have ordained it, women have been given almost equal status and opportunity with their male counterparts. The best examples of this are found during times of war. Women have replaced men in the factories, for example, and thus changed their roles in society:

> *Lloyd George went further in his search for more munition workers . . . They [suffragettes] marched down Whitehall with the slogan 'We demand the right to work'. Lloyd George gave them this right. Many hundred thousand women were brought into shell factories . . . typists in business and government; the male office-clerk vanished for ever . . . For the first time women were earning their own living on a massive scale. They went into public houses, and paid for their own drinks . . . There were women police . . . By the end of the war, it was no longer true that the woman's place was in the home.*

TAYLOR, 1963

These examples of the need to adapt to social changes during times of war

THE INDIVIDUAL IN SOCIETY

suggest that biology does not dictate male or female behaviour, but that in fact social influences play a greater part in shaping behaviour.

The Social and Cultural Explanation

Exponents of this theory do not believe that the roles of men and women are the same the world over; they would argue that it is the differences between men and women in different societies that determine the nature of gender divisions. These differences are learned through social processes and cultural influences and are therefore not genetically inherent. It is from the development of this theory that the word 'gender' has evolved, to separate the characteristics of biological differences from social factors. The biological differences (physiology and hormones, for instance) are encompassed within the term sex, while socially and culturally determined differences relate to gender. Gender differences are based largely upon the individual's behaviour and personality. It is important to note that sexual identity and gender should not be confused.

Sex typing must be distinguished from gender identity, which is the degree to which one regards oneself as female or male. A girl may have a firm acceptance of herself as a female and still not adopt all of the behaviours that her culture considers feminine or avoid all behaviours labelled masculine.

ATKINSON et al, 1990

Chapter 3 of Atkinson R L, Atkinson R C, Smith E E, Bem D J and Hilgard E R (1990) *Introduction to Psychology* (10th Edn). London: Harcourt Brace Jovanovich, Inc. addresses acquiring sex roles in more detail.

Which particular social and cultural influences create male/female divisions? Reference to your own gender roles may be a useful starting-point in answering this question.

It is important to stress that not all cultures serve to develop and promote the same roles. However, roles are primarily learned through a process of imitating the behaviour of significant others (social role modelling) and later this is reinforced by being identified with certain expected, social and cultural behaviour. The beginnings of this process occur during the primary socialisation of childhood, during which boys and girls may become 'sex-roled' and later 'sex-role stereotyped'. This is achieved by a variety of reinforcements:

Boys – as babies are dressed in blue
      – play with soldiers and cars
      – wear trousers

Girls – as babies are dressed in pink
       – play with dolls
       – wear dresses

As children grow older other reinforcements occur:

Boys – help father wash the car
      – go to football matches
      – play rough-and-tumble games using strength and requiring competition

Girls – help mother wash the pots
       – go shopping with mother
       – play more gentle games requiring dexterity and cooperation

Toys can provide some of the strongest reinforcers for roles and their characteristics. For example:

Boys – guns (aggression)
      – trains (masculine occupation)
      – football (masculine pastime)

Girls – dolls and dolls houses (home-maker)
       – nurse's outfit (feminine occupation)
       – embroidery set (feminine pastime)

There are numerous toys often considered to be for 'girls only', such as ironing boards and irons, vacuum cleaners, kitchen sets and so on. All can serve to reinforce the acquisition of the female gender role. Children will also observe the roles their parents perform, both within the home environment and in society at large, and this may lead to imitation of those roles by the children in later life. Kuhn, Nash and Brucken (1978) questioned children aged two to three years about gender roles. The responses outlined below represent those gender role stereotypes on which both boys and girls agreed:

Both boys and girls believed that girls:

- like to play with dolls

- like to help mother

- talk a lot

- never hit people

- say 'I need some help'

- will grow up to be a nurse or teacher

Both boys and girls believed that boys:

- like to play with cars
- like to help father
- like to build things
- say 'I can hit you'
- will grow up to be boss

The growth of feminism, equal rights movements and an increase in the numbers of men who readily perform so-called 'women's work' (the house-husband) has reduced some of the effects of sex and gender stereotyping but divisions still occur, especially in the labour market.

How does the acquisition of gender and sex roles affect the sexual division of labour; that is, the types of work available to women and men and opportunities for progression in the work environment?

This activity could have been approached from two separate, yet related, perspectives:

1 Where labour = paid employment external to the home environment.

2 Where labour = unpaid employment at home.

Within the former scenario women are often limited in their choice of occupation by male expectations of their abilities (men often being the actual employers). These expectations are frequently built on the belief that women have 'domestic roles' to fulfil and hence such expectations can be a restriction on the choice of work made available. Even when women 'prove' themselves to be competent in occupations, it can still be difficult for them to climb the management ladder. This point is well illustrated in nursing.

Nursing is one of the few occupations (and even fewer professions) which is numerically dominated by a female workforce. However, in the upper echelons of the hierarchical structure of nursing, where policy decisions are made, women are proportionately greatly under-represented (a situation repeated in many other areas of the labour market). The ending of the last decade and the advent of the 1990s brings new hope for women within the National Health Service (NHS). The British government launched into the next decade with an initiative to promote equality within the NHS. The initiative, titled *'Opportunity 2000: Towards a Balanced Workforce'* focuses on the needs of women, ethnic minorities and disabled people. This government policy document has been interpreted by the NHS Management Executive and it has developed a commitment to women published as *Women in the NHS* (DOH, 1991). This guidance document contains eight goals:

1 *Increase the number of women in general management to 30% by 1994.*

2 *Increase the number of qualified women accountants in the NHS.*

3 *Increase the number of women consultants to 20% by 1994.*

4 *Increase female representation on authorities or trusts to 35% by 1994.*

5 *Help women 'establish their own personal development needs' through a development centre.*

6 *Ensure that the number of qualified nurses and midwives leaving the profession does not increase.*

7 *Ensure women returning after maternity leave or a career break resume nursing on the same grade as they left.*

8 *Monitor the time taken for nurses to reach management positions.*

MASON, 1992

The fact that this guide exists emphasises a degree of inequality within the NHS. These recommendations, however, do not serve to advance equality between women and men to any major extent when the number of women who work in the profession is taken into consideration. As Mason acknowledges, target levels set at 30%, 20% and 35% are not proportional in a profession in which over 65% of personnel are women.

Follow-up surveys conducted after the initial launch suggest that few Health Authorities have shown any significant progress in implementing the government recommendations (Iganski, 1992). Ironically the current Minister of Health, Virginia Bottomley, who represents one of the few women in senior positions of power, gave her support to nurses by saying:

We are determined to be in the forefront of enlightened employment practices so that we can maximise the contribution of women in the service.

MASON, 1992

The position of women within industry and other areas of employment is similar. That is, they are poorly represented in management and restricted to providing labour within areas considered to be representative of their sex and gender, for example, hairdressing, shop-work and secretarial work. Additionally, when women do get access to an occupation considered to be a predominantly male area they rarely experience equality with male colleagues in areas such as pay, promotion, staff development and trade union representation. Allen (1993) argues that in order to enhance the position of women, it would be more fruitful to focus on differences between men and women in terms of access and power rather than in terms of attributes and skills.

Often women's employment efforts are viewed in terms of the 'second income' and are therefore accorded little status. Increasingly, however, women want to earn their own income, develop their own means of financial independence and the consequent freedom to make significant contributions to the family, if they have one, and be respected as individuals in their own right. That is, to exercise flexibility in their personal and professional lives. Allen points out that such flexibility places women in a position to cope effectively with the current radical change processes affecting the NHS. The subject of women's unpaid employment at home is no less controversial than that of paid work and raises many debatable issues in its own right.

Despite Taylor's observation in 1963 that a woman's place was 'no longer in the home', the sexual divisions of labour tend to reinforce belief that it is only 'natural' for women to stay at home and be the 'home-maker'. This belief reduces the opportunities for equality both outside and within the home. Is the labour of housework equally distributed where a man and woman live together? Housework is a strenuous and often poorly rewarded occupation which is frequently carried out by the woman of the house, even when both partners work. Cooking, washing up, washing clothes, vacuuming, dusting, washing windows, making beds, cleaning toilets . . . the list of household labour is almost endless even without the addition of child-care. Despite the supposed growth of 'the modern or new man' (men who perform so-called female roles) there would still appear to be a divide between male and female roles when accommodation is shared and especially in marriage. Oakley (1974) in her book *Housewife*, emphasises that the structure of modern families is still strongly patriarchal and that within marriage in Britain women do not have equality with men.

 You might like to share your reflections on this section with colleagues of the opposite sex. Discussion of your responses would no doubt prove to be both illuminating and insightful.

Even with the introduction of legislation such as the Equal Pay Act 1970, the Employment Protection Act 1975 and the Sex Discrimination Act 1975, sexual divisions still exist within society and continue to undermine the contribution and expertise which women provide, both within the home and to society at large.

This concludes the section on gender and the consideration of the relative positions of women and men in our society. The employment status of women has been addressed, particularly with regard to the NHS, and the next section builds on this knowledge in focusing on inequalities in health.

Inequalities in Health

*The problem of inequality in health (we) believe, lies at the
heart of the problem of better integrating British society . . .*

DHSS, 1980

If you have never before considered the notion of the existence of inequalities in health, it may be difficult to believe that inequalities can exist at all or to determine the nature of such inequalities. However, both research and commissioned reports have highlighted inequalities which exist in the provision of health services in Britain today.

As a nurse or midwife you may believe that excellence of practice, backed by a relevant knowledge base, will serve to reduce health inequalities. But such personal excellence can do little to reduce deep-rooted societal inequalities. Societal change will occur only through the collective action of significant professionals which ensures that a new set of 'norms' are adopted: norms which emphasise equity of provision, resource and infrastructure for health care systems.

This section aims to highlight inequalities in health, their nature and possible reasons for existence, as well as the inherent complexity of the situation. Before examining specific health issues, it would be advantageous to establish a base-line from which to work, and perhaps the best starting-point is to define 'inequality'.

Think about the word '*inequality*'. What does this mean to you? What ideas does the word conjure up in your mind? It may help to list words which you would use to describe the meaning of inequality.

Inequality relates to an absence of equality; to perceived or actual disparity, unevenness or variability. This suggests that where inequality exists, it exists at different levels or to different extents. Equally, people experience inequality with different degrees of severity and at different times. You may possibly have substantiated your description of inequality with reference to issues covered earlier such as race, sex, gender and social inequalities.

Having established a working definition for inequality, you can now focus on health.

What does inequality in health mean to you? What areas or issues do you think are central to 'health inequality'.

Many readers will have answered this activity from a personal perspective and possibly from that of their families. Often individuals will base their ideas about inequality on the choices and opportunities they think they have in their own lives. One example of this is the opportunity to gain a private education: rarely considered by parents who are low income earners, both because such education is not the norm for them and, obviously, because of financial constraints.

On the other hand, those parents who have themselves had a private education would consider the same schooling appropriate for their children. This would be their norm, if their current financial standing permits taking advantage of this opportunity. As we discussed elsewhere in this book norms are developed from many sources and are often very personal. This personal view can act as a barrier and make it difficult sometimes for the individual to perceive inequalities when they exist. For instance, do you feel that you have equality of *access* with others, to health provision and health care? Have you ever considered your *financial status* as being an advantage or disadvantage to your health? What about your *age*, or that of your relatives: could this lead to inequalities in health? Has your *education* influenced your health opportunities? What of your *social background* – could this be detrimental to your health or impinge on the opportunities for health gain of others? Have you considered *unemployment* as a possible cause of inequality in health? And if racial and gender inequalities exist, might not ethnic minorities and women in particular be faced with health inequalities?

In the previous section in this chapter on class, the relationship between class and health was examined. We now seek to examine health inequalities themselves. The central issues of concern are:

1 **Poverty**

2 **Access**

Both issues are related, of course, but for the sake of clarity they will be examined separately.

Poverty and Health

Poverty is a state that most people strive to avoid in their lives. For some it is an unacceptable concept that is rooted in the past, something that occurs in the world of Charles Dickens, or in Third World countries, but not in the contemporary Western world. Unfortunately, poverty exists in all nations regardless of size, population or international status. But what exactly is poverty?

Think about the concept of poverty and try to define it. What meaning does poverty have for you?

We suspect that almost without exception the main response will have been along the lines of: 'Poverty is to do with being poor'. However, as you are probably aware, this reply is too simplistic. Being poor, like being wealthy, is relative. For example, student nurses or student midwives when compared with nurse tutors would probably consider themselves poor. But in relative terms, students are themselves 'rich' in comparison to the unemployed. So where does poverty become a reality? Can it be an absolute state?

Over the years many sociologists and politicians have tried to define the realities of poverty. In the 1870s, Charles Booth in his work *Life and Labour of the People in London* (published in a shorter version in 1903) stated that poverty existed when a situation developed which made it impossible to live a healthy life, this definition being subsequently developed by Seebohm Rowntree. Between the years 1899 and 1950 Rowntree (1902, 1941, 1951) studied the people of York, and as a result of those studies defined poverty to be below the minimum provision needed to maintain health and working efficiency. This provision was primarily based on food, clothing and housing (or lack of these). Contributory factors included low wages, large families and unemployment. Rowntree also coined the term 'absolute poverty' to describe those who showed all the precipitating factors. In the 1960s Abel-Smith (1965) and Townsend carried out separate studies designed to measure 'relative poverty', the base-line being that income which the government believed to be the lowest level of income (supplementary benefits + 40 per cent) to sustain an adequate life. These studies indicated that over 14 per cent of the population lived in relative poverty and in 1979 Townsend's book *Poverty in the United Kingdom* suggested that few, if any, improvements had been made in combating such poverty.

Rowntree estimated that over 15 per cent of the York population lived in poverty, which at the time represented over 50 per cent of the working classes in the city, and this link with the working classes is still in evidence a hundred years later.

We have now illustrated the ideas of absolute and relative poverty and indicated that the effects of poverty are mainly felt by the working classes. Now we turn to considering what effect poverty has on individual health.

 Think about 'living in poverty' and how this might affect your health. It may be useful to begin by addressing issues such as diet, housing and clothing as suggested by Rowntree.

Given that income appears to be a crucial indicator of poverty it is clear that *money* is perhaps the single most significant factor. Money is required not only in order to buy clothes, pay rent (and other bills), and buy food, for example, it is also needed to socialise, to interact with others in society. The spending power of a person will also determine the **quality** of the products and commodities purchased.

Clearly, eating healthily is difficult, if not impossible for those in the 'poverty trap'. Apart from the expense of the nutritious types of food there is sometimes an ignorance of healthy diet . . .
'poor' people tend to eat the types of food their parents ate; often filling, fatty, stodgy and cheap . . .

BARRETT, 1990

Such patterns of eating coupled with poor housing do not encourage a healthy life-style. People living in poverty rarely own their homes, so they have to rely on the owners to make improvements or repairs. Heating can be expensive as can the purchase of appropriate clothing, and houses may often be cold or damp, or both. The allied cycle of health problems is frequently inherited and passes from generation to generation. This can result in both adults and children being at risk:

[the] . . . stresses of living on a low income increase the risk of parents having ill-health. This may make it harder for parents to look after the safety and health of their children.

FYSON, 1989

Access to Health and Education

The original intent, at the inception of the National Health Service in 1948, was to offer equal access to health care for all. The modern picture does not quite reflect this ideal.

In the 1980s, the people most at risk from ill-health and early death are those for whom preventive health services are least available and least used. These include families of unskilled workers, the poor in deprived inner city neighbourhoods, the homeless . . .

FYSON, 1989

Think about the above quotation, and identify why the people mentioned do not use the health services that are available.

General reasons would include the following:

1 **Timing of clinics** – these are frequently at times when people, especially working mothers, have difficulty attending.

2 **Atmosphere of clinics and surgeries** – often such environments are seen as imposing and threatening. Problems may be generated by poor communication between professionals and clients/patients.

3 **Lack of facilities for children** – too few clinics, surgeries and work environments provide adequate play/creche facilities for children. Many of those in need of health services have large families to consider.

4 **Uncomfortable waiting areas** – this relates not only to physical discomfort but also to social discomfort. Waiting areas are too often crowded, unstimulating and full of people with different backgrounds, behaviour and needs to one's own.

5 **Cost of transport to and from clinics** – for some people travel to clinics can be a major drain on financial resources. This factor is exacerbated by the centralisation of services within one district area, the contemporary model for provision of hospital health services.

6 **Language barriers** – the multicultural nature of our society demands that recognition be given to the communication needs of people for whom English is not their first language. Absence of appropriate help acts as a barrier to access of health care services for those individuals affected.

There is a substantial amount of evidence to support the reasons given for poor access; for example Barrett (1990) points to research which indicates that GPs do not give the poor parity of time and effort in comparison with more wealthy patients. Walsh (1984) illustrated the challenge posed by the Black Report which asked whether medical and nursing professions dominated by white, middle-class people could communicate effectively with city residents who were often perceived as inarticulate, were poorly educated and often from different cultural backgrounds.

Such a situation is not confined to Britain for as Jones and Jones (1975) argue, where physicians in the United States of America feel closely aligned intellectually and in terms of value systems with middle-class and upper-class patients they are reluctant to locate their practice in areas of poverty and deprivation.

The Black Report highlighted many of the issues addressed in this section and additionally emphasised the relationship between inequalities in society in general and inequalities in health:

> *Class differences in mortality for all adults aged 15–64 are somewhat less marked than in childhood, BUT this conceals a large difference for those in their twenties and thirties, and a smaller disadvantage for those approaching pension age . . .*
> *The risk of death in class V is between one-and-a-half to two times the risk in class I for adult males and females.*

DHSS, 1980

The Final Point

In 1986 the British Government produced a policy document entitled *The Health of the Nation: a Strategy for Health in England* (DHSS, 1986). This White Paper heralded a strategy which was to be based on health education and promotion, improvement in diagnosis, treatment and rehabilitation, plus a commitment to improving the quality of the environment. To achieve these objectives high standards of health services would be required, as well as changes to many people's life-styles. A further issue of the White Paper addresses the need for effective public policies in order to sustain and promote the nation's health. The need is recognised to utilise the suggestions and recommendations of the World Health Organisation and the European Community, in the pursuit of health gain for all.

To make the vision of a healthy nation a reality the government is promoting the role of such institutions as the NHS, the Social Services, the Health Education Authority, local education, the media and voluntary organisations. Effective, regular research is to play a vital role in monitoring the nation's health needs.

The proposals contained in *The Health of the Nation* are intended to improve the health of every man, woman and child irrespective of race, ethnic origin, sex, religion or wealth. However, the NHS has been striving to achieve this outcome since its inception in 1948 and, as you have discovered in this chapter, the various divisions in society can and do make it difficult, and sometimes seemingly impossible, for people to attain the degree of health equality which the White Paper hopes to promote.

Clearly health inequalities exist, and as a nurse or midwife you will soon be at the forefront of those trying to reduce the divisions that have helped to create such inequalities. Your effectiveness as a practitioner will be enhanced by your awareness of the influence of social divisions on health. The future may hold for you a role within care management/service planning areas; a future within which social inequalities will be key factors in deciding appropriate service purchase and provision.

References

Abel-Smith B (1965) *The Poor and the Poorest: A New Analysis of the Ministry of Labour's Family Expenditure Surveys of 1953–54 and 1960.* London: G Bell & Sons.

Allen C (1993) Women in public. Viewpoint, *Nursing Standard* 7(25): 42–43.

Atkinson R L, Atkinson R C, Smith E E, Bem D J and Hilgard E R (1990) *Introduction to Psychology*, 10th edn. London: Harcourt Brace Jovanovich.

Barrett C (1990) Poverty and health. *Nursing Standard* 4(22): 43.

Blane D, Davey Smith G and Bartley M (1993) Social selection: What does it contribute to social class differences in health? *Sociology of Health and Illness* 15(1): 1–15.

Blaxter M (1976) *The Meaning of Disability: A Sociological Study of Impairment.* London: Heinemann Educational.

Booth C (1903) *Life and Labour of the People in London.* London: Macmillan.

Brown C (1984) *Black and White.* Policy Studies Institute. London: Heinemann Education.

Cassidy S (1988) *Sharing the Darkness. The Spirituality of Caring.* London: Darton, Longman and Todd.

Coates K and Silburn R (1970) *Poverty: The Forgotten Englishmen.* Harmondsworth: Penguin Books.

Department of Health (1991) *Women in the NHS – an Action Guide to the Opportunity 2000 Campaign*. London: HMSO (NHS Management Executive).

DHSS (1980) *Inequalities in Health – Report of a Research Working Group*. London: HMSO (The Black Report).

DHSS (1986) *The Health of the Nation*. London: HMSO.

Disabled Persons (Employment) Act, 1944. London: HMSO.

Employment Protection Act, 1975. London: HMSO.

Equal Pay Act, 1976. London: HMSO.

Foreman J B (ed) (1975) *Collins English Gem Dictionary*. London/Glasgow: Collins.

Fyson N L (1989) *Poverty in Britain and the World*, 2nd edn. London: Hodder and Stoughton.

Halsey A H (1980) *Origins and Destinations: Family, Class and Education in Modern Britain*. Oxford: Oxford University Press.

Haralambos M (1985) *Sociology, New Directions*. Ormskirk: Causeway Press Ltd.

Hargreaves D H, Hester S K and Mellor F J (1975) *Deviance in Classrooms*. London: Routledge and Kegan Paul.

HMSO (1981) *West Indian Children in our Schools* (The Rampton Report). London: HMSO.

Iganski P (1992) Inequality Street. *Health Service Journal* 20 February 1992: 26–27.

Illsley R (1986) Occupational class, selection and the production of inequalities. *Quarterly Journal of Social Affairs* **2**: 151–161.

Jackson B and Marsden D (1962) *Education and the Working Class: Some General Themes raised by a Study of 88 Working Class Children in a Northern Industrial City*. London: Routledge and Kegan Paul.

Jones R K and Jones P A (1975) *Sociology in Medicine*. London: The English Universities Press Ltd.

Kuhn D, Nash S C and Brucken L (1978) Sex role concepts of two and three year olds. *Child Development* **49**: 445–451.

McNaught A (1988) *Race and Health Policy*. New York: Croom Helm.

Marx K (1867) *Das Kapital*. Moscow: Foreign Languages Publishing House.

Marx K (1888) Theses on Feuerbach. In Marx K and Engels F (1968) *Selected Works in One Volume*. Moscow: Progress.

Mason P (1992) Women's Movement? *Nursing Times* **88**(6): 17.

Morris D (1967) *The Naked Ape*. London: Cape.

Nisbet R A (1967) *The Sociological Tradition*. London: Heinemann Educational.

Oakley A (1974) *The Sociology of Housework*. London: Martin Robertson.

Oakley A (1976) *Housewife*. Harmondsworth: Penguin Books.

Oakley A (1980) *Women Confined: Toward a Sociology of Childbirth*. London: Martin Robertson.

O'Donnell G (1987) *Work out Sociology*. Basingstoke: Macmillan Education.

Open University (1985) *D102. Social Sciences – A Foundation Course. Block 3. The Production of Social Divisions*. Milton Keynes: Open University Press.

Rowntree S B (1902) *Poverty: A Study of Town Life*, 4th edn. London: Macmillan.

Rowntree S B (1941) *Poverty and Progress: A Second Social Survey of York*. London: Longman.

Rowntree S B (1951) *Poverty and the Welfare State: A Third Social Survey of York Dealing only with Economic Questions*. London: Longman.

Sex Discrimination Act, 1975. London: HMSO.

Smith A (1970) *The Wealth of Nations*. Harmondsworth: Penguin Books.

Smith D J (1977) *Racial Disadvantage in Britain – The PEP Report*. Harmondsworth: Penguin.

Taylor A J P (1963) *The First World War – An Illustrated History*. London: Hamilton.

Therborn G (1976) *Science, Class and Society: On the Formation of Sociology and Historical Materialism*. London: New Left Books.

Tiger L (1969) *Men in Groups*. London: Nelson.

Townsend P (1979) *Poverty in the United Kingdom: A Survey of Household Resources and Standards of Living*. Harmondsworth: Penguin Books.

Townsend P, Phillimore P and Beattie A (1986) *Inequalities in Health in the Northern Region: An Interim Report*. Northern Regional Health Authority and University of Bristol.

Walsh M (1984) City life, ONE – Black revisited. *Nursing Times* **80**(7): 48–50.

Whitehead M (1987) *The Health Divide: Inequalities in Health in the 1980s*. London: Health Education Council.

Wilkinson R G (ed) (1986) *Class and Health: Research and Longitudinal Data*. London: Tavistock.

CHAPTER 3

Labelling Theory and Stigma

The Earth does not argue,
Is not pathetic, has no arguments,
Does not scream, haste, persuade, threaten,
  promise,
Makes no discrimination, has no conceivable
  failures,
Closes nothing, refuses nothing, shuts none out.

WALT WHITMAN (1819–1892)

3 Labelling Theory and Stigma

Introduction

Welcome to this chapter on labelling theory and stigma. Its purpose is to help you to develop your knowledge of the societal use of labels, both positively and negatively, and to examine how these applications of labels affect the individual. Stigma can be the result of the labelling process and we therefore examine this concept later in the chapter.

To give you an overall sense of direction, we set out the objectives for reference both now and as you work through this chapter.

Objectives

After working through each part of this chapter we intend that you should be able to:

1 Understand how the concepts of **labelling, stereotyping, prejudice** and **discrimination** are central to labelling theory and stigma.

2 Identify how and why **labels** are used in society.

3 Describe the effect that the **labelling process** has on individuals.

4 Understand the nature of **social stereotyping**.

5 Identify the ways in which **labels/stereotypes** can both establish and maintain **prejudice and discrimination**.

6 Explain the potential conflict between **personal values and professional action**.

7 Apply what you have learnt about labelling theory and stigma to the consideration of **helpful relationships** with patients/clients.

Let us now begin examining the key concepts.

Labels

Before considering why and how labels are used, and the consequent effects of such use, let us first examine what labels are and what they tell us.

What's in a Label?

Labels are socially constructed phenomena designed to inform the observer. That is, while labels have physical characteristics such as the paper that they written on and the writing itself, they also have different meanings for different people. The meanings attached to labels are social constructs resulting from the interaction between individuals and their environment. As these interactions with the environment differ between individuals, so do the meanings that become attached to the same label. But what is the nature of the meaning attached to a label – what information do labels convey?

List all the information that a label conveys to you . . . (10 separate points would be a good list to aim for). It may help to think of the labels found on consumer products e.g. those found in your local supermarket.

The information may include:

- Country/place of origin
- Sell-by date
- Producer name/logo
- Quality
- Quantity
- Cost
- Function
- Ingredients/composition
- Volume/weight
- How to cook
- How to serve – food
- How to wash, iron or dry – clothing
- Safety instructions
- Value for money

These then, are examples of the information found on labels and you may have thought of many others.

The work of Felicity Stockwell serves well to illustrate the application of labels to patients by nurses. A study conducted in general hospital wards found that those patients with some kind of defect and those who had been in hospital for more than three months figured significantly in the 'unpopular' group. Additionally, the personality of the patient was found to be a significant factor in determining whether they received the labels of 'popular' or 'unpopular'.

> *Frustration and impatience were expressed about patients who grumble, moan or demand attention, also irritation about patients considered to be wasting their time. Psychiatric patients were overtly rejected or ridiculed.*
>
> STOCKWELL, 1972

Stockwell also quotes the work of Sarosi who applies characteristics to the labels of 'good' and 'bad' patient. The 'good' patient possesses attributes such as emotional stability, cheerfulness, ability to communicate with nursing staff, cooperation, appreciation of the services provided, conformity to rules and regulations and gives thought to the nurse's perspective. The 'bad' patient exhibits emotional instability, is a poor communicator, challenges and asks questions and wishes to maintain her independence. She may be aggressive, unappreciative, lack patience, be non-conformist and fail to adopt the nurse's point of view.

A recent report from Canada (Grief and Elliott, 1994) identified how nurses in Accident and Emergency departments quickly categorised patients depending on the behaviour and reasons for attending. Moral evaluation by health care professionals was cited to be a regular feature of medical settings and such evaluations were held to affect the treatment given to patients directly. Trauma victims or patients with surgical problems constituted a preferred group while those patients categorised with some responsibility for their condition, such as drink drivers or individuals who had deliberately overdosed, were rated unfavourably.

One nurse in the study is quoted as saying 'I expect people to take control and responsibility for their lives . . . I do not tolerate well those who continue to be fat, smoke, not take their meds, drink and otherwise abuse their bodies'.

This application of characteristics to a label will be addressed further, later in the chapter. Interestingly, contemporary images of a patient would value the presence of 'bad' characteristics such as independence, questioning and active involvement in nursing actions. Similarly anxiety and hostility are recognised as common reactions to admission to hospital and show psychological needs in the individual. Peterson, while not acknowledging current perceptions of the totality of patient/client needs, succinctly expresses the true status of the 'unpopular' or 'bad' patient:

> *Actually a difficult patient is one whose needs are not met — emotional, physical or both.*
>
> PETERSON, 1967

Perceptions

Labels, then, contain information but as we have already learned this information can be interpreted differently by different individuals. Interpretation follows perception of the information. One cannot interpret without first perceiving.

 How does the information you listed in the previous activity affect your perception of the product?

As labels affect perceptions, so perceptions in turn affect the behaviour of individuals. For example, because 'value for money' is of prime concern for many, they may like to buy a product which they can afford, and which meets their needs. But we also purchase goods on the basis of subjective whim or preference as opposed to the potentially more objective criterion of 'value for money'. An example of this process is the purchase of 'designer' suits or dresses which might be seen as poor value for money, given that remarkably similar items can be obtained much more cheaply elsewhere. Such purchasing behaviour is undoubtedly guided by the label attached to the item and in particular the 'name'. Labels, then, affect your perceptions of the product and these perceptions in turn cause differing kinds of behaviour to occur in response to the product. The same process of response, in this case to a product, is of course also applicable to the labels attached to people.

Charles Handy (1985) talks of the work of Harold Kelly who studied the effect of prior impressions on perception and behaviour. Prior to a psychology session at the Massachusetts Institute of Technology, the student group was given information about a replacement tutor. This information contained details of the tutor's qualifications, teaching experience, age and social background. Additionally, in secret, half the student group was told that he was considered to be a cold person and the other half was told he was a warm person. After the session the students evaluated the tutor's performance. Those who had been told the tutor was a warm person rated him higher in terms of consideration, informality, sociability, popularity, nature, humour and humanity than those who were told he was a cold person. Analysis of the class dynamics during the session showed that 56 per cent of the 'warm' students actively participated while only 32 per cent of the 'cold' students did. This illustrates how the information presented can affect the perceptions of the people involved and their subsequent behaviour.

Behaviour

Labels enable us to make 'sense' of our work, to deal with the complexity of stimuli and activity which are a part of our daily lives. In this sense labels have a positive use; they facilitate order out of chaos, reduce uncertainty and help us to act. For example, when presented with an object labelled 'anal thermometer' we are empowered to act through understanding its purpose and additionally its mode of use. This would be true even if the thermometer were a different shape from those previously experienced; the label would provide sufficient information for us to identify the object and thus act.

However, as well as this positive aspect of the label, there is a negative counterpart. The use of labels is a double-edged sword. That is, the labelling process can engender negative perceptions in, and thus negative behavioural responses from, individuals.

Stereotyping

One of the results of labelling is stereotyping. Stereotypes are closely associated with the attitude held by individuals. As outlined in Chapter 1, attitudes have three components:

1 Cognitive – what the person thinks/believes.

2 Affective – what the person feels.

3 Behavioural/conative – what the person does/has a tendency to do.

Stereotyping is related to the cognitive component, i.e. the thought-processes or beliefs of individuals. The belief, however must be held by more than one individual in order to be a stereotype.

Atkinson et al (1990) *Introduction to Psychology*, 10th edn. pp. 314–315. London: Harcourt Brace Jovanovich.

The above book gives the following definition of a stereotype:

> *A stereotype is a packet of inferences about the personality traits or physical attributes of a whole class of people.*

Thus we infer in, or attribute to, groups of people certain physical or personality characteristics.

McGhie A (1973) *Psychology as Applied to Nursing,* 6th edn. pp. 124–126. London: Churchill Livingstone.

McGhie (1975) additionally gives us the following:

> [a stereotype is] *a generalised and over-simplified belief or opinion which tends to be resistant to contradictory facts.*

In other words, we may perceive, and thus behave towards, a whole group of people in a simplistic way, such behaviour often being the result of hearsay, guesswork or indirect experience. Even if we *directly* experience the group – for example, working with them – we may still persist in our stereotyping despite evidence to the contrary. Thus an intelligent Irishman may be perceived as 'out-of-the-ordinary' or 'different' from the others.

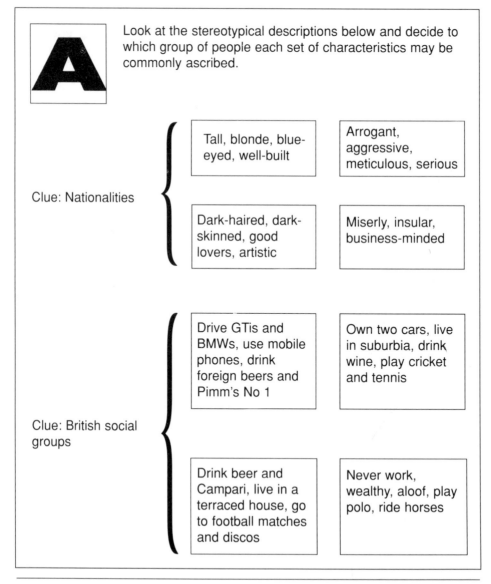

A

Look at the stereotypical descriptions below and decide to which group of people each set of characteristics may be commonly ascribed.

Clue: Nationalities

Tall, blonde, blue-eyed, well-built	Arrogant, aggressive, meticulous, serious
Dark-haired, dark-skinned, good lovers, artistic	Miserly, insular, business-minded

Clue: British social groups

Drive GTis and BMWs, use mobile phones, drink foreign beers and Pimm's No 1	Own two cars, live in suburbia, drink wine, play cricket and tennis
Drink beer and Campari, live in a terraced house, go to football matches and discos	Never work, wealthy, aloof, play polo, ride horses

Suggested possibilities might include:

1 Scandinavians/Swedish?

2 Germans?

3 Italians?

4 Jews?

5 Yuppies?

6 Middle-class?

7 Working-class?

8 Upper-class?

In this exercise we gave you the characteristics and you applied labels. Used positively, this process enables us to make sense of a disparate range of characteristics and is one that is commonly used in medical diagnosis. For example, the term 'myocardial infarction' is the label applied to a set of physical characteristics, knowledge of which enables both the doctor and nurse to act. Once we know what it is, we know how to act. Similarly, the process is applied in mental health to give us labels such as schizophrenia and depression and in the field of learning disability with regard to such conditions as Down's syndrome and Apert's syndrome. Each of these labels conjures up a set of allied characteristics which guides our activities and programmes of care. You might like to consider whether programmes of care based on sets of characteristics can be truly individualised? Or whether the use of 'medical labels' is an essential means of communication?

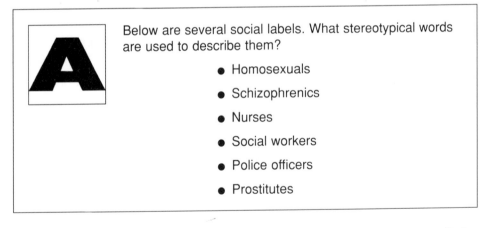

A Below are several social labels. What stereotypical words are used to describe them?

- Homosexuals
- Schizophrenics
- Nurses
- Social workers
- Police officers
- Prostitutes

In this activity you were asked to carry out the inverse process of the preceding activity. That is, you were applying the characteristics to the label as opposed to applying the label to the characteristics. This last activity, applying the characteristics to the label, becomes one of stereotyping if, as our definitions stated earlier, it is based on inference rather than fact and done simplistically or superficially.

You may well have found yourself using both 'positive' and 'negative' stereotypes. For example, nurses are often seen as 'angels' or 'caring' – a positive stereotype – while homosexuals are also often though of as 'deviant', 'abnormal' or 'carriers of sexually transmitted diseases' – a negative stereotype.

In both of these activities you might have completed your work without conscious reflection on the reasons behind your answers. To assist in avoiding the use of negative stereotypes or labels, and in thinking objectively, you might find it useful to ask yourself the following when assessing a person, group or situation:

- why do I think as I do?

- why do I behave as I do?

- how does my behaviour affect others?

- have I got all of the information I need in order to act?

Asking such questions facilitates self-awareness, awareness of one's own thoughts and behaviour and how these affect others. As nurses it is important that you are self-aware, that you understand how your self-perception affects both your behaviour towards others and how you interpret their behaviour.

Alice, in *Alice's Adventures in Wonderland*, (Carroll, 1971), illustrates self-awareness during a conversation with the caterpillar. When asked who she is, Alice replies that she is no longer sure, having changed several times in the course of that morning. Health professionals subject to rapid changes in the health environment may well experience similar doubts regarding their role identity.

How much do you think the actual role of the nurse is determined by publicly held stereotypical images? Do we act as we do because people expect us to? How does the public image affect our self-image?

We have been considering the functions of stereotypes – that is, what purpose they serve. Now we shall move on to examine the origins and maintenance of stereotypes.

Note down how you think our stereotypical images develop. Also, think about how these influences affect our attitudes towards others.

Make notes on how *your* attitude may influence others, especially in your professional role as a nurse.

The following are recognised to be important elements in both the formation and maintenance of stereotypes:

- Parents
- Schooling
- Peers
- Mass media
- Friends
- Personal experiences
- Personal prejudicial thought
- Expectations
- Positive reinforcement of images
- History
- Colleagues
- Professional influences
- Religion
- Politics
- Moral standing
- Culture
- Ethnic origin
- Sex/gender

As a nurse you may be affected by such influences as working in a multicultural society, helping those who you do not personally like, the views of patients/clients/parents, the pressure from colleagues to 'conform' and the diktats of the medical profession.

Your attitude to these influences may be reflected in turn in your own behaviour. Examples might be showing favouritism to certain patients/clients, role-modelling inappropriate behaviour to junior nurses, or allowing subjective preference to interfere with professional practice. This last issue will be covered in more detail later in the chapter.

Summary

Stereotyping is the simplistic application of group perceptions, the result of which may be either positive or negative behaviours.

Prejudice

Beck R C (1986) *Applying Psychology: Understanding People,* pp. 238–266. London: Prentice Hall.

Beck (1986) writes of stereotyping as: 'assigning specific traits to an entire group of people, without consideration of individual differences.' The author then goes on to define prejudice as follows:

> *Prejudice refers to a preconceived attitude toward the members of some group formed only upon the basis of their membership in that group.*

Prejudice is an emotional manifestation rather than the outcome of reason. The affective component of attitudes, mentioned in the section on stereotyping, is the predominant factor at play. Whereas stereotypes are founded in the cognitive component of attitudes, that is, what we believe or think, prejudice is an emotional reaction to an object or situation with little or no reasonable basis. Attitudes based upon emotion tend to be very rigid and resistant to modification. When people refuse to alter their attitudes in the face of contradictory evidence one can reasonably suppose the existence of prejudice.

Prejudice, however, is not necessarily limited to negative attitudes; positive prejudices do exist, e.g. positive discrimination in favour of certain ethnic groups with regard to job opportunities or educational opportunities. Unfortunately, prejudice has become associated with a negative meaning and it is this aspect of prejudice that you will be examining.

Stereotyping and prejudice are clearly linked and we have already seen how these behaviours can be the result of the application of a given label. Applying a label then, even in all innocence, can often lead to unfounded prejudice.

Reflect upon the common prejudices that exist in our society.

You may well have found this exercise easy to complete and were able to make well-defined responses similar to those of your colleagues who attempted the exercise. On the other hand, the task may have proved difficult for you. The level of difficulty will undoubtedly have been related to self-awareness, of your personal prejudices, and awareness of your environment.

Certain groups in our society, though, are widely recognised as being on the receiving end of prejudice on a frequent basis. Such groups include:

- Ethnic minorities (due to either skin colour or racial origin)
- Religious sects
- Political organisations
- Women
- The unemployed
- People with learning disabilities
- Homosexuals
- AIDS sufferers
- People with mental health problems
- The 'working classes'

Now that we have acknowledged the existence of prejudice in our society, it will be useful to have an understanding of its origin, development and maintenance.

Intergroup Conflict

Minority groups attempt to improve their status within what is to them an alien society. For example, the Ugandans who escaped the excesses of the Amin regime in the 1970s had migrated to the United Kingdom in order to 'start afresh'. In terms of status these people were then at the bottom of the social ladder and have striven to improve their position since. A similar process occurred with the West Indian migrants of the 1950s and the Asian migrants of the 1960s. However, this need to 'improve' creates conflict with the indigenous population because of the increased competition which results, in areas such as employment and housing.

Personality Factors

Personality, and its description, tends to provoke controversy. Research by Adorno et al (1953) during and after the Second World War, apparently identified personality characteristics in individuals that seem to be related to prejudice. They identified what was termed the Authoritarian Personality, the type of person who becomes a Nazi, whose main tenets were said to be anti-semitism, political and economic conservatism, ethnocentrism, and authoritarianism. Such a personality, however, does not carry prejudice in isolation; rather it is reinforced by a network of other attitudes and beliefs which support it and serve to give confirmation to it. The authoritarian personality is said to view the world in rigid black-and-white categories:

> *Either you are a member of their group and one of them or you are*
> *a member of some other rejected group and must be against them.*
> BARON AND BYRNE, 1977 *cited in* BECK, 1986

Baron and Byrne (1977), cited in Beck (1986), categorise three aspects of social interplay which illuminate the origins of prejudice:

1 Intergroup conflict

2 Personality factors: the authoritarian personality

3 Social learning

Discuss with your colleagues and make notes in the boxes about the nature of each of these factors and why prejudice results from them. You might find the examples given at the top of the boxes useful as a starting point. See also Beck (1986), pp. 260–262.

---

1 *Intergroup Conflict*, e.g. as a result of the immigration of Ugandans into the United Kingdom in the 1970s

---

2 *Personality Factors: the Authoritarian Personality*, e.g. the type of person it takes to be a Nazi

---

3 *Social Learning*, e.g. mass media's reinforcement of prejudice

Social Learning

During the socialisation process of early childhood we are subjected to the attitudes, both positive and negative, of others. These 'others' will include parents, peers, teachers and the mass media. These influences shape our own attitudes as we imitate the role models in our lives. So the prejudices of our role models become ours also, through the process of socialisation.

Summary

The formation of prejudice, then, is the result of a number of interacting factors. Additionally, the concepts of prejudice and stereotyping are inextricably linked. It is worth while spending some time reflecting on our own prejudices. Perhaps you feel you have none? Maybe the process of reflection will uncover prejudices you never thought you had? Or are you already aware of your prejudices . . .?

Discrimination

Both stereotyping and prejudice are essentially states of mind. That is, they may not harm others unless actually acted upon. The notion of 'action' is what differentiates prejudice and discrimination.

 Beck R C (1986) *Applying Psychology: Understanding People*, pp. 258–260. London: Prentice Hall.

Beck (1986) gives a definition for discrimination as follows:

> *Discrimination refers to* negative actions *against the members of a group toward which there is a prejudice.*

Discrimination thus provides the final component of an attitude – the behavioural/conative component (what the person does or has a tendency to do). The three components of an attitude thus far discussed are illustrated in Figure 3.1.

ATTITUDE COMPONENTS

Cognitive component
(What the person thinks or believes) ——————————— Stereotype

Affective component
(What the person feels) ——————————— Prejudice

Behavioural/conative component
(What the person does or has a tendency to do) ————— Discrimination

---

Figure 3.1. Attitude Components.

 As nurses we may discriminate against individuals. Think about how this discrimination process may occur, and why, and the effects that such action may have on the individual.

How might such discriminatory action also be detrimental to yourself and the nursing profession?

Undoubtedly you will have generated a variety of answers to this activity, which may have included the following ideas and probably some others:

How may discrimination occur?

- Subjective bias towards some patients/clients – spending less time with others.

- Carrying out only the bare necessities for some patients/clients while 'doing everything' for others.

- Conversing with some patients/clients and not others.

- Poor assessment of some people's needs.

- Implementing inappropriate care practices that have no relation to individual need.

- Not communicating the needs of the person discriminated against to others.

- Not truly advocating for some clients/patients with other members of the care team.

Why may discrimination occur?

- The person poses a 'threat' to your professional action.

- The person questions your knowledge and skills.

- The patient/client does not 'follow orders' or planned programmes of care.

- Negative past experiences of 'similar' people or groups.

- Personal prejudices and stereotypes.

- Inappropriate direction from more experienced staff.

- Pressure from colleagues to 'conform' to discriminatory practices.

Effects of discrimination on the individual?

- Anger.
- Frustration.
- Feeling of helplessness.
- Loss of choice.
- Inability to make decisions.
- Restriction of opportunities.
- Loss of individuality.
- Needs are not met.

Effects of your discriminatory practices, with others, on self?

- Guilt (if actions are recognised).
- Attribution of negative characteristics to yourself by those discriminated against and potentially by colleagues who are non-discriminatory.
- Distortion of ability to practise effectively.
- Possible action due to contravention of the UKCC Code of Conduct.

Effects of discriminatory practices on the nursing profession?

- You are seen, by the general public, both as a 'person' and a 'nurse'. Consequently if negative characteristics are attributed to you personally, these characteristics may also be applied to the nursing profession. Thus the individual discriminated against may develop a prejudiced attitude towards *all* nurses which may adversely affect any future relationships between the two parties.

Research supports the presence of some of the discriminatory practices described above. Stockwell associates discrimination with the application of the labels 'popular' or 'unpopular'. Nurses responded to 'popular' patients with 'rewarding' behaviour:

- Willingness to give more time
- Allowing a more personal interaction
- Willingness to accept gifts and favours
- Allowing lapses in keeping the rules

'Unpopular' patients were subjected to 'deterrent' behaviour:

- Ignoring the patients
- Forgetting patients' requests

- Refusing gifts and favours
- Enforcing rules
- Using sarcasm

Similarly, recent research conducted by Harris and Russell (1992) for the Department of Health illuminates issues raised by the attribution of 'aggressive behaviour' to people with a learning disability. A common response from service providers to individuals so labelled has been custodial care, which the researchers argue is inappropriate. Harris and Russell found that such individuals did not need secure accommodation as much as they needed new and effective services within the community setting.

They also express a strong belief in the link between the manifestation of aggressive behaviour and the person's quality of life.

> *In general, supportive, compensatory and normalising environments helped eliminate aggressive behaviour whereas deprived, stressed and unstimulating circumstances exacerbated early problems.*

HARRIS AND RUSSELL, 1992

The work of Harris and Russell seriously questions the application of the label 'aggressive behaviour' to people with a learning disability and highlights the effect of the applied label on the behaviour of others with whom they are in contact. Subsequent service provision is also challenged.

Further information on the work of Philip Harris and Oliver Russell can be found in the following documents:

1 *The prevalence of aggressive behaviour amongst people with learning difficulties (mental handicap) in a single health district,* Interim Report, January 1989
2 *The nature of aggressive behaviour amongst people with learning difficulties (mental handicap) in a single health district,* Second Report, July 1989
3 *Rising to the challenge? The lives of five people with very challenging behaviour,* Third Report, March 1990
4 *An evaluation of services for four people with learning difficulties and aggressive behaviour,* Final Report, May 1992

All the above reports were published by the Norah Fry Research Centre, Bristol University.

Summary

Discrimination primarily has negative effects on the people on the receiving end of the process, but it may also result in unforeseen consequences for the discriminator. People may discriminate for a variety of reasons, but there is a clear link between the concepts of stereotyping and prejudice and the action of discrimination.

Stigma

There is one last concept that needs addressing at this stage and that is the notion of stigma. The *Shorter Oxford English Dictionary*, Third Edition (1968) gives the following definition of stigma:

> *A mark of disgrace or infamy; a sign of severe censure or condemnation, regarded as impressed on a person or thing . . . a distinguishing mark or characteristic (of a bad or objectionable kind).*

This definition arises from the sixteenth-century practice of branding or marking criminals, or unstable members of society, so that they could be readily recognised. The definition given is not totally applicable to the concept of stigma as applied in contemporary fashion. What it does acknowledge, however, is that in some way some members of society apply bad or objectionable characteristics to other individuals. Thus people are 'stigmatised' by an attached label. As Argyle (1983) states, some individuals, such as homosexuals, ex-convicts, mental patients and members of disreputable professions, conceal their identities from others in order to avoid social rejection; to avoid stigmatisation. Here, Argyle is pointing out that people can be stigmatised and as a result of this process their behaviours can be altered.

Goffman in Scheff (1967) describes stigma as consisting of several basic types. Stigma arising from racial, national or religious origins are cast as tribal stigmas. There are also stigmas attached to the physical characteristics of the individual including those wrongly attached to the characteristics of women and older people. Finally we have those stigmas attached to what is seen as moral irresponsibility. Such stigmas become applied to individuals who are unemployed, suffer from alcoholism or addiction, or with a history of sexual deviation or mental disorder.

Much has also been written about the stigma of illness. For example Altschul and Sinclair (1986) talk of the historical evidence of disgust and rejection of sickness which still persists.

To be healthy is praiseworthy, to be ill can be regarded as shameful, wicked or a sin. The strength of the 'work ethic' in our society can lead to sick people being seen as malingerers or 'spongers'. Hence these people will often feel guilt or shame about their illness and will be unable to discuss it with others.

One group in our society which has undoubtedly suffered from stigmatisation are people with a learning disability. Society has an expectation that all citizens, including those with learning disabilities, will adhere to social norms. However, because of stigmatisation stereotypical views are held of people with learning disabilities and these restrict their opportunities to experience and develop social norms for themselves. This process in turn reinforces the stigma attached to people with learning disabilities: that they cannot achieve or are abnormal in some way. Through this process the stigma becomes a self-fulfilling prophecy or vicious circle, as illustrated in Figure 3.2.

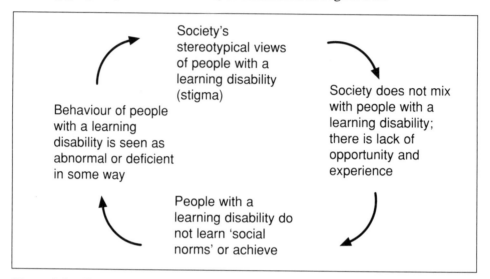

Figure 3.2. The self-fulfilling prophecy.

Edgerton describes vividly the effects of stigmatisation in his studies of the lives of people with a learning disability (referred to by him as 'mental retardates') who were discharged from the Pacific State Hospital in California:

> *The stigma of having been adjudged a mental retardate is one which the ex-patients in this study reject as totally unacceptable. Hence, their lives are directed toward the fundamental purpose of denying that they are in fact mentally incompetent. These former patients must at all times attend to the practical problems of seeming to others to be competent and of convincing themselves that this is so. The label of mental retardation not only serves as a humiliating, frustrating, and discrediting stigma in the conduct of one's life in the community, but it also serves to lower one's self-esteem to such a nadir of worthlessness that the life of a person so labelled is scarcely worth living.*

EDGERTON, 1967

You might like to reflect on this quotation when considering the impact of the closure programmes for the large mental health and learning disability hospitals in the United Kingdom, implemented during the 1980s and 1990s. Could one of the results have been the sudden confrontation of people with their own limitations and fallibilities? Did such moves into the community shatter people's belief in their levels of competence? Or did all benefit from a newly-found quality of life?

Edgerton also points out that because so many ex-patients find an admission of mental retardation so totally unacceptable they resort to using other highly stigmatising explanations for their behaviour and previous admission to the hospital. Examples are given of individuals referring to themselves as 'crazy' or 'epileptic' in preference to admitting mental incompetence. Edgerton speculates that this occurs because:

> . . . no other stigma is as basic as mental retardation in the sense that a person so labelled is thought to be so completely lacking in basic competence.
>
> EDGERTON, 1967

Once the incompetence of a former patient becomes, in Goffman's words 'evident' or 'obtrusive' the 'normal' person talks down to the individual and tends to speak both more slowly and loudly than ordinarily, (much as people do when holidaying in foreign climes and attempting to communicate without knowledge of the relevant language). As a result, interaction and communication are reduced to simplistic levels which assume little experience and even less ability. Any meaningful interaction becomes almost non-existent.

There are clear implications in Edgerton's words for the maintenance of effective communication with your patients/clients. It can be just as easy to treat the individual admitted to a medical ward as 'incompetent', from the height of your professional knowledge and skill-base, as Edgerton suggests it can be with the person designated a mental retardate.

As illustrated earlier in Figure 3.2 assumptions made about the competence of patients/clients can lead to certain kinds of behaviour, in our example ineffective communication, influencing opportunities for achievement. The 'poor performance' resulting from this lack of opportunity further strengthens the initial assumptions made (in the vicious circle).

This is how one former patient expresses the effect of stigmatisation:

> I don't believe that anyone from the hospital has it easy outside. There's problems from being in that place. I mean with people you meet. They take me as if I'm not a smart person. That's what makes me so provoked. And I mean they act like I don't understand things, which I do understand things. That's a terrible thing; I'd never do that to anybody. I don't know why I have to suffer like this. Sometimes I'd rather be dead than have people act like I'm not a smart person.
>
> EDGERTON, 1967

Summary

Stigmatisation, as with stereotyping, prejudice and discrimination, can lead to negative lifestyles for certain individuals. Such lifestyles tend to worsen problem areas rather than helping the individual come to terms with them. Edgerton (1967) argues that it is impossible to understand truly the lives of people with a learning disability without recognising the extent to which stigma dominates their lives.

Personal Values and Professional Action

In discussing labelling, prejudice, discrimination and stigma the importance of personal action has been emphasised. Within the section on discrimination we also began to touch on the issue of professional action. Often the drive for personal action and that for professional action can be in conflict when the nurse or midwife experiences incongruence between their personal values and those of the profession. As Steele and Harmon state: to hold true to personal values becomes difficult when pressurised to adopt conflicting professional values. Such conflict results in the development of both frustration and dissatisfaction.

Personal and professional values are not the only source of incongruence. Patients/clients also hold values of their own which may conflict with those of the nurse/midwife. The drive toward patient-centredness, to uphold the rights of clients, creates the potential for discrepancy between the personal and professional value systems of the nurse and the value systems of the patient/client. As the client exercises their decision-making rights the discomfort felt by the nurse can only be relieved by giving the client's values higher priority than their own (Steele and Harmon, 1979).

The professional values of nurses, midwives and health visitors are expressed via the United Kingdom Central Council for Nursing, Midwifery and Health Visiting (UKCC) Code of Professional Conduct. The clauses within the Code of Professional Conduct that seem to be particularly relevant to the topic areas of this chapter include:

> *Clause 1* – *act always in such a manner as to promote and safeguard the interests and well-being of patients and clients.*

> *Clause 7* – *recognise and respect the uniqueness and dignity of each patient and client, and respond to their need for care, irrespective of their ethnic origin, religious beliefs, personal attributes, the nature of their health problems or any other factor.*

> *Clause 8* – *report to an appropriate person or authority, at the earliest possible time, any conscientious objection which may be relevant to your professional practice.*

> UKCC, 1992a

Burnard and Chapman (1993) illuminate the meaning of Clause 1 arguing that professionals give individual service to the client and in doing so raise the client's needs above their own.

Clause 7 emphasises the individual nature of current approaches to care and recognises the rights of people entering into health-care systems. Care professionals are urged to respect the customs, spiritual beliefs, values and life-styles of their clients/patients. Failure to acknowledge the uniqueness of individuals, their inherent differences, may lead patients/clients to question their self-concept and ultimately expose themselves to insecurity and doubt. The examination of differing cultures, custom, beliefs and values enables nurses/midwives to develop a perspective of their own as well as to understand that of others. Impersonal approaches contradict the establishment of equal partnerships between health professionals and those in their care. Burnard and Chapman cite Styles as saying:

> *I believe in nursing as a humanistic field in which the fullness,*
> *self-respect, self-determination, and humanity of the nurse*
> *engage the fullness, self-respect, self-determination and the*
> *humanity of the client.*
>
> STYLES *in* BURNARD AND CHAPMAN, 1993

The UKCC's *The Scope of Professional Practice* expands on Clause 7 when it states:

> *Practice must . . . be sensitive, relevant and responsive to the*
> *needs of individual patients and clients and have the capacity to*
> *adjust, where and when appropriate, to changing circumstances.*
>
> UKCC, 1992b

Clause 8 of the Code of Professional Conduct upholds the right of the nurse/midwife/health visitor to express conscientious objections to aspects of their work. However, it also places the responsibility on the health care professional to make known their objections to the appropriate other people at the earliest opportunity. Burnard and Chapman illustrate the difference between professional judgement and conscientious objection through the consideration of the application of Electro-convulsive Therapy (ECT). This is a mode of treatment indicated primarily for those individuals suffering from psychotic depression and for whom other available treatments seem to have little positive effect. Basically, a controlled charge of electricity is given to the anaesthetised individual via electrodes applied to the temples. This electrical charge induces a short convulsive episode which for reasons which are not entirely clear appears to have a beneficial effect for some patients in lifting their depression. The nurse may exercise professional judgement in this situation by expressing that a person is not physically fit to receive ECT on this occasion, while considering the treatment justified in normal circumstances. (It is standard procedure for patients to have a full physical assessment prior to ECT.) The nurse's professional judgement may or may not be accepted by medical staff.

Alternatively, the nurse may object to ECT on the grounds that it is morally wrong to administer a treatment that knowingly disrupts normal brain functioning. This is a conscientious objection.

While Clause 8 offers the opportunity to make known conscientious objections it does not give the nurse/midwife the right to opt out of practice situations without consulting others. It is important that nurses/midwives are able to clarify their own values in order to avoid conscientious objections being made irrationally and 'blindly'. In a professional context nurses and midwives should be able systematically to support their objections and not act on a personal whim.

Clause 8 offers the health professional no legal right to refuse to participate in treatment other than for the termination of pregnancy (not including subsequent care) under the terms of Section 4 of the Abortion Act 1967. The UKCC offers the following guideline:

> . . . any practitioner should be careful not to accept employment
> in a post where it is known that a form of treatment to which
> she has a conscientious objection is regularly used.
>
> UKCC, 1989

The UKCC also advises that the health care professional is entitled to make their position clear but must recognise that doing so may have implications for their contract of employment. In addition, while a conscientious objection can be made in a situation which enables managers to make alternative staffing arrangements, it cannot be applied to emergency treatment.

Recently practitioners have indicated the wish to refuse to participate in the delivery of care to patients/clients with certain conditions – not objecting to the nature, form or appropriateness of a treatment for the condition but to the condition itself. Examples include those patients/clients with Acquired Immune Deficiency Syndrome or hepatitis B infection. The UKCC have made a statement on their position in this situation:

> . . . the Code of Professional Conduct does not provide a
> formula for being selective about the categories of patient or
> client for whom the practitioner will care. To seek to be so
> selective is to demonstrate unacceptable conduct. The UKCC
> expects its practitioners to adopt a non-judgemental approach in
> the exercise of their caring role.
>
> UKCC, 1989

Religious beliefs often raise areas of conflict between nurse/patient and nurse/nurse and because of this nurses need to appreciate the basic differences between differing faiths and also ways of living without a set of religious beliefs. In the same way that values may conflict with professional responsibilities so may religious beliefs. But this is not simply a question of right or wrong.

> A situation which places the nurse in a struggle between religious
> beliefs and professional responsibilities does not require a choice

between right and wrong. It is a struggle between two 'goods' each of which is valuable in certain situations. The nurse of Roman Catholic faith may well experience an incompatibility between the values of her/his religious affiliation and the values of the client/patient. Both values are good in their own context but incompatible in this situation.

STEELE AND HARMON, 1979

Levine, cited by Steele and Harmon, argues that the practising nurse assumes ethical responsibility in every dimension of practice. This argument is continued when the point is made that the excellence of nursing practice can be measured by the 'moral commitment' that the nurse makes to her/his patient/client. If professional nursing embodies ethical responsibility then it requires ethical decision-making. A decision-making process might look as in Figure 3.3.

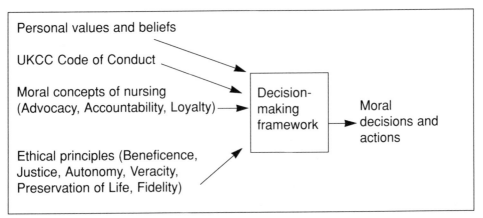

Figure 3.3. Adapted from Creasia and Parker, 1991, p. 158.

Thus, while the nurse's personal values and beliefs are important contributions to the decision-making process, they by no means represent all the essential factors.

 Many ethical decision-making frameworks are available for use. You might like to investigate Jameton's 'Method for Resolving Nursing Ethics Problems' which is outlined in Creasia J L and Parker B (1991) *Conceptual Foundations of Professional Nursing Practice*. London: Mosby Year Book.

All health care professionals are encouraged to question, to argue, to challenge when necessary.

In the field of health care delivery, it is essential that the practitioners who are thoughtful far outnumber the ones who are thoughtless if the consumers are to receive humanistic care where the concept of client (patient) as person prevails.

STEELE AND HARMON, 1979

However, the professional who questions solely on the basis of personal values walks on fragile ground.

. . . whatever position one holds, that of other people is equally valid. A nurse is on difficult ground if she condemns others for the values that they hold and even more difficult if that condemnation is verbalised. Such behaviour is not in keeping with the Code of Conduct nor with the process of caring for others.

BURNARD AND CHAPMAN, 1990

Helpful Relationships

Our final objective for this chapter talked of using the materials presented and the knowledge gained to establish helpful relationships with your future patients and clients.

 This is the time to reflect on what you have learned from working on this chapter. Use your learning to decide now how you can avoid the negative effects of labelling, stereotyping, prejudice and discrimination in your future career as a nurse/midwife. It may help to think about preventing labelling and stigma – how you could do this and what methods you might use.

You might like to set yourselves goals for achievement in these areas or use such goals to construct an Action Plan for yourself (a document outlining your intended actions – which is regularly reviewed or evaluated and modified as necessary).

We have chosen to present our thoughts on this last activity in two sections entitled 'Questions and Action'. The first of these, Questions, is intended to cause you to stop, think and reflect before you act, and the second section, Action, gives you some ideas on how to act following this phase of reflection.

Questions

- Do I apply labels negatively or inappropriately?

- Do I really understand the meaning behind the labels that I use?

- Do I understand how the use of a label may cause me to lose sight of the essential 'human' qualities of the people I nurse?
- Do I hold stereotypes about other people?
- Am I prejudiced against other people?
- Do I discriminate unfairly against others either personally or professionally?
- Do I understand the consequences of my behaviour?
- Do I truly know how my behaviour affects others?
- Am I able to perceive the stigma attached to certain people that I socialise with/work with/care for?
- Am I able to minimise such stigma in my care practices?
- Am I happy that my patients/clients can trust me to be objective in my dealings with them?

Action

- Reject the given label or;
- Change the label to a less derogatory term or;
- Change the value attached to a label.
- Break the vicious circle of labelling by rejecting the automatic acceptance of the assumptions underlying labels.
- Think about the individual – not the group.
- Apply individualised plans of care – do not rely on routine and tradition.
- Discuss perceived instances of stereotyping, prejudice and discrimination with colleagues in the care team.
- Understand and use the Equal Opportunities policy of your organisation in all your practices.
- Ask patients/clients about *their* experience of the care provided (this should be part of a Quality Assurance programme).
- Ask for, and participate in, awareness days on issues such as stereotyping, prejudice and discrimination if you feel that these are necessary.
- Make it your responsibility to teach/inform/enlighten junior staff with regard to these issues.

Act impartially, objectively and skilfully using a sound knowledge base – be professional and aware

Conclusion

Within this chapter we have attempted to address a wide range of issues. We have considered the use of labels in our society how labels can help us to make sense of our world but also be applied inappropriately. Similarly, we have explored the concept of stereotyping which, used positively, enables us to structure our lives. Used negatively, however, stereotyping leads us to make unreasonable assumptions about people in our society and can lead to prejudice and discrimination. We differentiated between stereotyping plus prejudice and discrimination by saying that the former two concepts are primarily cognitive processes while the latter constitutes action of some sort. From stereotyping, prejudice and discrimination arises the wider concept of stigma – the tainting of individuals with negative characteristics – this stigma leading to lack of opportunity for development and to under-achievement. Finally, we considered the idea of helpful relationships and how you could attempt to ensure that such relationships are part of your future activities.

You may have noticed that the major section headings in this chapter illustrate the vicious circle, or causal loop, found within Labelling Theory and Stigma. This loop is outlined in Figure 3.4.

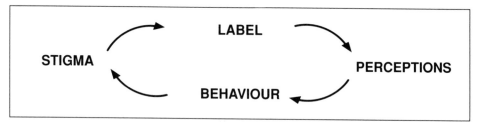

Figure 3.4.   Causal loop – labelling theory and stigma

Thus negative use of these concepts becomes a self-fulfilling prophecy, as we saw earlier in this chapter. Implementing helpful relationships enables you to avoid the degrading effects of the causal loop shown above and provides a more positive causal loop of its own, as shown by Figure 3.5.

Figure 3.5.   The question/action loop

This loop suggests that you should question, or assess, the situation and plan before you act, or implement. Subsequently your acts should also be questioned, or evaluated for effectiveness before any further action is taken. Thus we are systematically trying to avoid labelling and stigma using the approach known as the *Nursing Process*. The stages of the nursing process approach are identified in Figure 3.6.

THE INDIVIDUAL IN SOCIETY

Figure 3.6. The nursing process

We hope that the information contained in this chapter has proved interesting and will be of use in the future. There is a need to put the individual before the label, to give priority to assessed needs above supposed characteristics, if you are to be effective, both as nurses and people, in the future. There is also a clear need to recognise your own personal values, and those of the profession, in order truly to understand those of the patient/client:

> *The goal of values clarification is to facilitate self-understanding.*
>
> STEELE AND HARMON, 1979

We will leave you with one last example of the labelling process as manifest in nursing. Phil Ratcliffe, in a stimulating article on the use of language in nursing, outlines the work of Rosenhan who investigated labelling in the field of mental health in the following manner.

> *Rosenhan arranged for nine healthy volunteers to present themselves at various psychiatric hospitals. They complained of hearing voices. Once admitted, they ceased to simulate any symptoms and told staff they felt well and did not require treatment. In spite of this, eight were diagnosed as having schizophrenia and one as having manic depression.*
>
> *All were stereotyped as insane, with staff talking over their heads and treating them as incompetent. One nurse wrote of a subject who kept a diary of his experiences: 'The patient continues to exhibit writing behaviour'.*
>
> RATCLIFFE, 1993

> *Every variety of philosophical and theological opinion was represented there [the Metaphysical Society], and expressed itself with entire openness; most of my colleagues were -ists of one sort or another; and however kind and friendly they might be, I, the man without a rag of a label to cover himself with, could not fail to have some of the uneasy feelings which must have beset the historical fox when, after leaving the trap in which his tail remained, he presented himself to his normally elongated companions. So I took thought, and invented what I conceived to be the appropriate title of 'agnostic'.*
>
> T H HUXLEY (1825–95)

References

Adorno J W, Frenkel-Brunswick E, Levinson D J and Sandford R N (1953) *The Authoritarian Personality*. New York: Harper and Row.

Altschul A and Sinclair H (1986) *Psychology for Nurses*, 6th edn. London: Baillière Tindall.

Argyle M (1983) *The Psychology of Interpersonal Behaviour*, 4th edn. Harmondsworth: Penguin Books.

Atkinson R, Atkinson, R E, Smith E E, Bem D J and Hilgard E R (1990) *Introduction to Psychology*, 10th edn. London: Harcourt Brace Jovanovich.

Beck R C (1986) *Applying Psychology: Understanding People*. London: Prentice-Hall International (UK).

Burnard P and Chapman C M (1990) *Professional and Ethical Issues in Nursing – The Code of Professional Conduct*. Chichester: John Wiley & Sons.

Burnard P and Chapman C M (1993) *Professional and Ethical Issues in Nursing – The Code of Professional Conduct*. 2nd edn. London: Scutari Press.

Carroll, L (1971) *Alice's Adventures in Wonderland and Through the Looking Glass and What Alice Found There*. London: Oxford University Press.

Creasia J L and Parker B (1991) *Conceptual Foundations of Professional Nursing Practice*. London: Mosby Year Book.

Edgerton R B (1967) *The Cloak of Competence – Stigma in the Lives of the Mentally Retarded*. London: University of California Press.

English National Board (1985) *The Individual in Society – Caring for People with Mental Handicap – a Learning Package for Nurses, section 1*. London: ENB.

Getzels J W (1958) Administration as a Social Process. In Halpin A W *Administrative Theory in Education*. Chicago: University of Chicago.

Goffman E (1967) Normal Deviants. In: Scheff T J (ed) *Mental Illness and Social Processes*. London: Harper and Row.

Grief L and Elliott R (1994) Emergency nurses' moral evaluation of patients. *Journal of Emergency Nursing* 20(4): 275–279.

Handy C B (1985) *Understanding Organisations*, 3rd edn. Harmondsworth: Penguin Books.

Harris P and Russell O (1992) How to meet a challenge. *Health Service Journal*, 8 October, 28–29.

Huxley T H (1979) *The Oxford Dictionary of Quotations* 3rd edn. Oxford: Oxford University Press.

McGhie A (1975) *Psychology as Applied to Nursing*, 6th edn. London: Churchill Livingstone.

Onions C T (ed) (1968) *The Shorter Oxford English Dictionary*, 3rd edn. Oxford: Clarendon Press.

Peterson D I (1967) Developing the difficult patient. *American Journal of Nursing*, 522.

Ratcliffe P (1993) Mind your language. *Nursing Standard* 7(20): 44.

Steele S M and Harmon V M (1979) *Values Clarification in Nursing*. New York: Appleton-Century-Crofts.

Stockwell F (1972) *The Unpopular Patient*. London: Royal College of Nursing.

UKCC (1989) *Exercising Accountability – A Framework to assist Nurses, Midwives and Health Visitors to consider Ethical Aspects of Professional Practice*. London: United Kingdom Central Council for Nursing, Midwifery and Health Visiting.

UKCC (1992a) *Code of Professional Conduct*, 3rd edn. London: United Kingdom Central Council for Nursing, Midwifery and Health Visiting.

UKCC (1992b) *The Scope of Professional Practice*. London: United Kingdom Central Council for Nursing, Midwifery and Health Visiting.

CHAPTER 4

Institutions and Institutionalisation

An institution is the lengthened shadow of one man.

RALPH WALDO EMERSON (1841)

4 Institutions and Institutionalisation

Introduction

The purpose of this chapter is to help you to develop your knowledge of institutions, the roles that these play in our society and the effects of institutions, and their practices, on the individual. We shall also be considering how you, as a nurse, can both recognise the effects of the institution on the individual and take steps to militate against such effects where they may adversely influence individual health and quality of life.

To give you an overall sense of direction you may like to read the following objectives and refer to them as necessary during the future activities associated with this chapter.

Objectives

After working through each part of this chapter we intend that you should be able to:

1 Define the components of an **institution**.

2 Define the concept of **institutionalisation**.

3 Describe the role that institutions play in society.

4 Identify the effect that institutions, and the process of institutionalisation, may have on the individual.

5 Outline societal attitudes regarding institutional care.

6 Describe how institutions and institutionalisation affect the caring process.

7 Describe the nurse's role:

- within institutional care settings;

- in reducing the potentially negative effects of institutionalisation on individual health and quality of life;

- in ensuring that institutionalisation does not occur.

Let us now begin to examine the key concepts involved in institutions and institutionalisation.

Institutions

As we saw earlier, sociologists and psychologists have long been concerned with the task of trying to explain the behaviour of groups and of those large aggregates of people known as societies. As we have learned, they have attempted to address the central notion of structure versus agency – that is, to what extent behaviour is determined by societal structures or alternatively to what extent people are self-determining. In examining the regularities of human behaviour two contrasting explanations may be offered:

1 The role of Institutions, focusing on the behaviour of groups.

2 Modal personality types (culture is said to produce a 'modal' or common personality type). The focus here is on individuals.

Sociologists who emphasise the role of institutions are adopting a 'macro-social' perspective in order to explain social integration and address the issues of conformity, consensus and conflict within society.

 At this stage it would be useful to consider your perceptions of the meaning of the word 'institution'.

Make some notes explaining what you think an institution is.

In response to this exercise you may well have written about physical structures, e.g. buildings and the activities within them. This, of course, would be appropriate and represents the popular image of institutions in our society. In sociology, however, institutions have been given a far greater significance than being mere physical structures. We can begin to understand this significance if we look at some definitions of institutions.

Defining Institutions

The Concise Oxford Dictionary defines 'institution' as:

> . . . *established, law, custom, or practice; familiar object; organisation for promotion of some public object; building used by this . . .*

FOWLER AND FOWLER, 1967

THE INDIVIDUAL IN SOCIETY

Already it appears that physical structures such as buildings are only a small element of what is encompassed by the word 'Institution'. A further definition is given by Collins Contemporary Dictionary (1984), as follows:

> *. . . an established law, custom, or public occasion;*
> *. . . an organised pattern of group behaviour established*
> *and generally accepted as a fundamental part of the culture . . .*

Here the emphasis is on group behaviour and combined with the first definition given presents a picture of this group behaviour being directed towards a purpose, object or goal.

Herriot (1976) describes the institution as a system of practices and social roles organised around a series of values. In addition a framework exists with which to regulate and administer practices and set roles. The introduction of values acknowledges that group behaviour does not only reflect objective purpose but that such behaviour may be the expression of underlying value systems which are shared by large groups in society.

Finally Thompson et al (1975) argue that institutions are not mere aggregates of values, customs, practices, laws, social roles and activities but rather that they serve to achieve a goal or function.

Institutions in Society

Edward Shils (1975) argues that society holds together because it has a 'centre' and a 'periphery'. The 'centre' is crucial and consists of the dominant major institutions in society which maintain a pattern of roles and activities into which people are bound. Of greater significance to Shils, though, is that these institutions sustain between them a set of common values, beliefs and symbols. The 'centre' defines roles and values for the rest of society. But because the 'centre' also carries 'authority' it is able to legitimise those values and beliefs that it supports and thus maintains.

In modern political science emphasis is placed upon three main institutions and the role that these play in society:

1 The legislative or government;

2 The judiciary or law; and

3 The executive or bureaucracy.

Politics is often viewed as the resolution of a conflict between the inherent forces of violence and revolution in society and the existing legislative, judicial and executive institutions. By means of consensus and compromise, or the use of power and force, a balance is achieved. The point along a given spectrum at which this happens governs the character of the state – either increasingly disorganised or increasingly institutionalised. Figure 4.1 presents institutions as being associated with organisation and hence stability and social order.

Increasing disorganisation   Increasing organisation

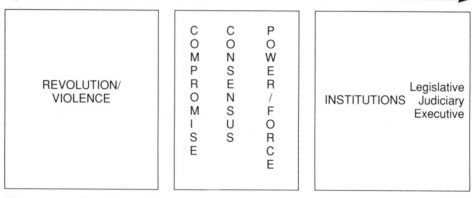

Figure 4.1. The state and the role of institutions

William H. Whyte in Pugh et al (1986) has approached the use of values by institutions through the concept of 'the social ethic'. This ethic, he believes, provides moral justification for the pressures society places upon individuals to behave in prescribed ways. The 'social ethic' holds that the individual is meaningless alone, but that by being absorbed into the group he or she can create a whole that is greater than the sum of its parts. Whyte believes that scientific, academic and business institutions tend towards the 'social ethic' in our society. Consequently, group consciousness is valued more highly than individual genius. Here, one could argue, is an example of institutional practices governing behaviour on the basis of a societal value.

In addressing why people comply with or conform to orders and standards of behaviour, Amitai Etzioni (1961) focuses on the instrumental or purposive nature of social institutions and organisations. Formal organisations such as those in government, business or education have a need to achieve goals and because of this need an emphasis is placed upon performance and making sure that behaviour is in line with the required performance. Organisations are said to ensure compliance to required behavioural standards in two ways:

1 Through hierarchies of power and authority issuing rewards and penalties, e.g. society has legal institutions issuing fines and imprisonment for non-compliance and educational institutions give degrees and diplomas, as rewards for high educational performance.

2 Ensuring that members of the organisation are committed to its aims and purposes – motivation through involvement, e.g. a democratic government institution allows involvement in determining the aims and purposes of our society.

Think about your previous experiences in institutions or organisations (for example, in an educational or business institution). Can you identify how these institutions influenced your behaviour, i.e. in what specific ways did they exercise power over you? How did they get you to do things?

Maggs C J (1989) *Exploring History – An Introduction to Nursing's Past*. Continuing Nurse Education Project. An Open Tech Project, p.51, Extract 6.
This extract illustrates well the 'abuse' of 'treatments' and many other texts on nursing history carry similar stories.

Your answers to this exercise probably involved focusing on a wide variety of specific influences which will be related to your individual experience. Pugh et al (1986) outline three types of power which organisations and institutions use to ensure compliance to required standards of behaviour:

1 **Coercive** – the possible use of force or action, e.g. the historical use of drugs and unpleasant 'treatments' in asylums to do away with undesired behaviours.

2 **Remunerative/utilitarian** – the manipulation of material resources which the person desires, e.g. businesses may manipulate salaries and performance bonuses or hospitals might withdraw staff privileges, such as 'unofficial' tea-breaks, in order to reduce undesired behaviour.

3 **Normative/identitive** – manipulating symbols such as love, affection, prestige and loyalty. This use of power is often found in religious organisations, universities and voluntary associations. An example in nursing might be where the symbolic 'caring' function of the nurse is manipulated through the voicing of a sentiment such as 'Nurses don't strike because they care', or beginning a statement with, 'If you really cared . . .' in order to produce the desired behaviour.

These are examples of what can be called *visible powers*. In an article entitled 'Powers Visible and Invisible', Rob Paton talks of 'institutional bias' as a form of invisible power (Paton et al 1987). Paton argues that in organisations and institutions individuals and groups are provided with scope to pursue certain goals and restricted in pursuing others. For instance, educational facilities might be biased towards certain teaching and learning styles giving precedence to them over others which are limited or even denied altogether to both students and teachers.

Reflect upon your learning experiences either at school, in a further or higher education establishment, or as a student nurse/midwife. Do you think your educational institution prefers/preferred certain teaching/learning styles?

If so, why might this be/have been so? Do you feel that the teaching/learning styles adopted are/were restrictive or facilitative?

If you compared your answers with other respondents there would undoubtedly be variation in your experiences. This might be reflected in the mention of a variety of teaching/learning styles or different feelings about the benefits of a particular teaching/learning style. Some of this variety could be because you have attended a different educational institution from other respondents. If you attended, or are attending, the *same* institution variation may be due to individual preference, for example, or to teacher delivery.

If you felt limited, but were not really sure why, this might have been due to the invisible nature of 'institutional bias'. Such 'biases' can be considered an aspect of 'invisible' power because they may benefit some of the 'stakeholders' in an institution far more than others – those whose interests are well served through the existing arrangements. Normally, such groups will be dominant groups, but not always. Do you think the medical profession maintains 'institutional bias' within health services? Do nurses restrict patients/clients in ways which reflect 'institutional bias'?

Roles and Institutions

Some sociologists believe that we can best understand human behaviour by reference to the roles that individuals fill in our society.

The institutional approach, for example, suggests that we can best express ourselves by adopting one of the institutionalised roles which our society acknowledges. Thus sociologists such as Erving Goffman believe the individual to be 'a multiple-role performer'. We perform our roles to meet our social context, such roles being delineated by the institutions of our culture. Goffman additionally assumes that humans share the meaning of activities and situations and it is this fact that allows them to collaborate. In defining how people arrive at such shared meanings Goffman uses the analogy of a theatrical play.

Firstly, the *scene* is set, e.g. 'a family reunion' or 'an emergency admission to the accident and emergency department'. The *roles* are specified for people to play, e.g. 'the nurse', 'the patient', 'the receptionist'. These *roles* define the relationships between the actors. There is also a *plot* or *story*, i.e. the group share an idea of what is expected to happen. Finally, there is a *script* to guide participants through the *plot*, i.e. conventions as to how to speak and act and who will say and do what and when. These elements when combined are called by Goffman a *scenario*. Activities are consequently fairly patterned and life is a series of 'performances' in which we play larger or smaller roles in a scene.

Jot down some of the roles that you might play in your current lifestyle.

What kinds of behaviour and attributes are clearly expected of you in these roles? What kinds of behaviour and attributes are clearly not expected of you? Where do these expectations of your behaviour come from?

When the authors reviewed their current life-styles they found that the following roles immediately sprang to mind: Teacher, Father, Husband, Golfer, Son, Son-in-Law, Brother, Shopper, Counsellor, Writer and Student.

Within the role of Father, the author is expected to support and love his daughter (expected behaviour) while not abusing her mentally or physically (behaviour not expected). As a Teacher, the author is expected to be able to deliver knowledge to students but maybe not to possess the intellectual attributes of Albert Einstein or Aristotle (which is just as well, really!).

Many of the roles that we enact within scenarios are supplied by institutions. For example, the family is an institution consisting of the central roles of mother, father, child, brother, sister as well as grandparent, grandchild, aunt, uncle, niece, nephew, etc.

We also, however, draw heavily on culture in enacting roles. Hence, teachers may play 'traditional' roles such as the 'stern disciplinarian', the 'kind friend', or the 'weak, hopeless person'. Students, on the other hand, may be the 'swot', or 'bully', or 'dunce', or 'class clown'. These are standardised roles drawn from our culture and if we enact a role that does not fit cultural patterns other 'actors' may not respond and the performance will collapse; relationships between people will not work, for then social meaning is lost, activities and situations are not shared. Are the 'schizophrenic person' and 'the person with learning disabilities' playing culturally inappropriate roles which are not recognised by other 'actors'?

While emphasising the importance of roles, though, it is necessary also to acknowledge that we maintain a 'social identity' – personal long-term characteristics that we carry between scenarios. We all have a personal identity that we want others to perceive. This identity we try to achieve through aspects such as style of dress, speech and manner. Our social identity allows us to resist full submission to institutional power and to retain individual agency.

'A Study of Prisoners and Guards in a Simulated Prison' (Chapter 15) In: Potter D et al (1981) *Society and the Social Sciences*. Routledge and Kegan Paul, London, contains an account of an experiment conducted by Haney, Banks and Zimbardo. It illustrates vividly the power of institutions to determine roles and to shape our behaviour, attitudes, thoughts and feelings.

Meanings in different social situations are linked together in systematic ways. The roles in one institution connect with roles in others and the scripts share common assumptions because of the relationships between the institutions. The Open University (1986) describes society as numerous social scenes linked by:

a) culture which supplies scenarios and scripts

b) institutions which supply roles and

c) broad groupings which supply identities.

The changing of institutional roles and social indentities in turn changes people. However the possession of a social identity which bestows power on the individual also bestows choice and freedom; the power to exercise agency.

The Person Determined or Autonomous?

Walter Buckley, writing in *Systems Behaviour* (Open Systems Group, 1987), states:

> . . . *'institutions' may provide a normative framework prescribing roles to be played and thus assuring the required division of labour and minimising the costs of general exploratory role-setting behaviour, but the actual role transactions that occur generate a more or less coherent and stable working compromise between . . . the structured demands of others and the requirements of one's own purposes and sentiments.*

Until this point in the chapter, we may have given you the impression that our behaviour is very much determined by society and its institutions. The quotation from Buckley acknowledges that we do not merely conform to, but also act upon, our environment.

The article from which this quotation is drawn also discusses the work of Anselm Strauss et al which is described more fully in, *The Hospital and its Negotiated Order.* Strauss believes that social order is not simply a matter of automatically maintaining norms but something which needs 'working at'. Order within organisations Strauss chooses to call 'negotiated order'.

To illustrate this 'negotiated order', Strauss described a hospital organisation. Hospitals, like other organisations, have hierarchies of status, and power, rules, roles and goals. Complex interactions occur between different 'actors', such as doctors, patients/clients, psychologists, nurses, students, administrators and hotel services staff. Each of these people may have their own goals, ideologies and reference groups and command various degrees of prestige, esteem and power; consequently, they act differently.

Additionally, Strauss found that the rules governing the behaviour of these people were not binding, extensive or even known to many. The area of action covered by clearly defined rules was very small. Individual action was very possible around the general purpose of the hospital. This individual action was facilitated through negotiation between the professionals involved. Strauss's negotiation model presents a picture of the hospital – and perhaps most other spheres of social life – as a transactional milieu where numerous agreements are 'continually being established, renewed, reviewed, revoked, revised'.

The Functions of Institutions

During the previous sections we have given thought to the nature of institutions in our society and the importance accorded by some sociologists, and writers on organisations, to the concept of role behaviour within society. In doing this, we have mentioned some of the perceived functions of institutions. In this part of the chapter, we shall therefore repeat what we have said about those functions and, we hope, by introducing some new functions as well, give you a more comprehensive insight into the part that institutions play in our society. Thompson et al (1975) give us the following functions to consider:

1 A social institution simplifies action for the individual by transmitting uniform patterns of behaviour to individuals to enable them to meet certain situational contexts.

2 The standards and codes of the institution, thus transmitted, save the individual time and effort in decision-making and problem-solving. (**Note:** individuals may, however, be frustrated by too-rigidly-enforced behaviour patterns.)

3 By its shaping of individual conformity the institution is a strong medium of social control. Institutions act as stabilisers in the social order by regularising and standardising individual and group behaviour.

4 Institutions preserve the culture of the society – fundamental institutions such as the family and church change very slowly over time.

5 Institutions exist to perform specific functions for society, e.g. educational institutions protect, socialise and educate children, legal institutions maintain order, health institutions maintain the well-being of society's members, while business institutions produce and exchange goods and services. How these societal goals are achieved in practice – that is who does what, when and where, and how they do it – is largely determined by institutions.

These functions are not rigidly fixed prescribed actions, however. Processes within institutions may change with time passing, as may their structures and purposes. For example, the church has lost major functions of education and social work to the state.

Similarly, the family has largely handed over its former industrial–productive functions to business institutions and possibly its caring of elderly members to government institutions. These changes of purpose have in turn undoubtedly resulted in the evolution of new structures and processes within those business and government institutions.

In examining institutions as separate entities, it may seem that they operate in isolation from one another. This, of course, is not the case; they are interdependent, in that changes in one institution can have consequences for another. Examples of this interdependence include the effect that changes in government have on the educational, industrial and religious institutions and the far-reaching effects that the breakdown of economic institutions may have on other social institutions.

Institutions can be said to share common structural components, or elements, which however may manifest themselves differently given a specific institutional setting. Table 4.1 illustrates this point.

Within the list of functions given earlier the idea of uniform patterns of behaviour, or norms, was introduced. Those behaviour patterns in society which are well-established and accepted as a fundamental part of culture have been termed by Krech et al (1962) 'institutionalised ways'. These are a system of standard behaviour events, together with their associated beliefs, values and norms, which represent a society's solution to one of the main problems of living, e.g. dating rituals in our society which further the objective of procreation: or the upbringing of children; or the disposal of the deceased. Institutions enact norms in a variety of ways. Within the health service, for instance, new legislation (NHS and Community Care Act, 1990) has been enacted, and thus there are new norms, with the stated intent of improving services to patients/clients. If a norm is accepted, taken for granted, and conformed to by the majority it is said to have become 'institutionalised'.

The Hospital as a Social Institution

Historically, hospitals have always cared for the sick but they also functioned as shelters for the accommodation of pilgrims, the poor and the lame. Particular hospitals also provided the function of isolation: for example, for those suffering from leprosy, plague and syphilis. The need to perform this range of functions reduced the hospital to a low status and it was not until after the eighteenth century that reorganisation and modernisation occurred.

What do you think the functions of the hospital are in contemporary society?

List the functions you identify.

Undoubtedly, we have seen the move away from specialist health services isolated from one another. This has been reflected in the closure of hospitals

Institutional elements	Family	State	Church	Industry
Stated objectives and purposes	Procreation, social status, etc.	Provision of welfare, jobs, security and protection of rights	Establishment of good relations with supernatural	Providing income, occupation, generating wealth, etc.
Behaviour patterns, including attitudes	Love, affection, devotion, loyalty, parental respect, etc.	Devotion, loyalty, respect, obedience, etc.	Reverence, awe, fear, etc.	Fair play, thrift, workmanship, application, etc.
Symbolic traits	Wedding ring, crest, coat of arms, heirlooms, etc.	Flag, seal, emblem, anthem, uniforms, etc.	Cross, icon, idol, shrine, altar, hymn, etc.	Trademark, design, advertising emblem, etc.
Utilitarian traits	House furnishings, house, garden, etc.	Public buildings, public works, police, equipment, etc.	Temple, pews, baptistry, etc.	Stores, factories, ships, railroads, machinery, etc.
Oral or written tradition	Marriage licence, genealogy, etc.	Constitution, treaties, law, history, etc.	Bible, catechism. etc.	Contracts, franchises, articles of incorporation, etc.

Table 4.1. Adapted from Thompson L F et al, 1975, p. 125.

for people with either mental health disorders or a learning disability, and the relocation of acute mental health services on to the sites of large district hospitals. The general health needs of people with a learning disability are now met by these large district hospitals and thus we now have the model of a hospital meeting the health needs of adults, children, people with mental health disorders and people with a learning disability on one large central site.

The following specific functions of the hospital may also have been identified by you:

- To provide employment, and thus livelihood, for a range of professional and non-professional staff.

- To conduct clinical and statistical research into health and disease processes.

- To provide high quality and competent care for individuals when ill, in order to restore healthy functioning to the optimum level.

- To prevent illness and encourage healthy life-styles.

- To provide a learning environment for staff, e.g. for nursing and medical students.

- To meet the health needs of the citizens of the community when they are unable to take care of themselves.

- To develop and maintain highly effective specialised areas of health care.

- To develop new treatment and care strategies and organisational structures in the face of changing societal demands on the service.

- To provide the equipment necessary to aid effective diagnosis and treatment.

- To regulate medical and nursing practice (and that of other hospital staff).

- To provide an arena for multidisciplinary teamwork which takes advantage of a range of specialist skills.

This is obviously not a comprehensive list of functions but gives some indication of the current range of activities to be found within the contemporary hospital.

The Life Cycle of the Institution

Acknowledgement has already been given to change occurring in the structures, processes and functions of institutions. These elements of change can be the result of wider change related to the 'life cycle' of an institution. Sir Geoffrey Vickers describes this life cycle in the following terms

> *Institutions grow, repair themselves, reproduce themselves, decay, dissolve. In their external relations they show many characteristics of organic life . . .*
>
> VICKERS G, *cited by* OPEN SYSTEMS GROUP, 1987

Thompson et al (1975) go on to describe stages in the life cycle of an organisation. Figure 4.2 is a graphic representation of these stages.

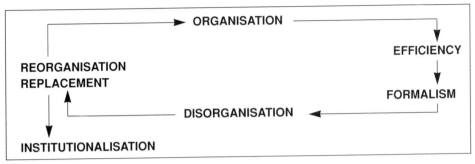

Figure 4.2. The life cycle of an organisation.

The five stages of organisation, efficiency, formalism, disorganisation and reorganisation/replacement can be described thus:

Stage 1 – the need for the institution becomes apparent and groups begin to organise. Leaders, codes, role definitions and functions emerge.

Stage 2 – the institution is accepted and its functions carried out, usually with enthusiasm and efficiency.

Stage 3 – various codes and ideologies become more or less fixed in the institutional structure.

Stage 4 – the institution loses most of its flexibility and becomes less vital in meeting the needs of the group.

Stage 5 – reorganisation of the institution, or replacement of it with a new one, is necessary in order to move through the cycle once again to the efficiency stage.

If Stage 5 is not successfully completed, institutionalisation occurs, a state in which attitudes, traditions, symbols and codes become so fixed that change is almost impossible without revolutionary methods. Routine, instead of ensuring smooth running, now means decay. (You will be asked to think more about this process of institutionalisation later in the chapter.)

Summary of Societal Institutions

Modern institutions foster qualities that are required of people in modern societies. Institutions serve to integrate society through the interdependent nature of their role sets (complements of related roles) and their transmission of the central values of society. The mass media and the educational system, for instance, are both engaged in the production and/or dissemination of ideas, values, beliefs and social knowledge. Our view of the world is fundamentally shaped by these two institutions. Their permeation of the whole of society and their direct linkage with the state, or centre of society, facilitates the shaping of societal values and subsequently of an integrated society.

During this part of the chapter you have already considered the interaction between the individual and societal institutions. This interactional process leads to observed kinds of behaviour and is illustrated in Figure 4.3.

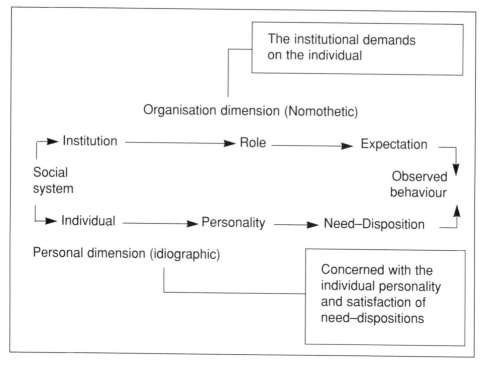

Figure 4.3. Behaviour in a social system, adapted from Getzels J W (1958). Reproduced with kind permision of McGraw Hill.

Institutionalisation and 'The Total Institution'

Institutionalisation can be defined as the characteristics of life in an institution. These characteristics will be examined in detail later, but first it is necessary to explore the factors that make an institution what it is, and why these establishments are set aside by society as being different from other congregations of people.

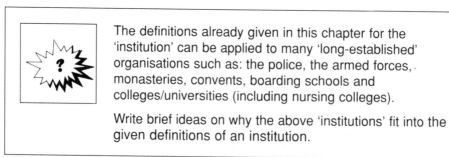

The definitions already given in this chapter for the 'institution' can be applied to many 'long-established' organisations such as: the police, the armed forces, monasteries, convents, boarding schools and colleges/universities (including nursing colleges).

Write brief ideas on why the above 'institutions' fit into the given definitions of an institution.

We suggest that the organisations listed below can be considered to be institutions because of the following characteristics.

Boarding schools

- Separated from mainstream establishments.

THE INDIVIDUAL IN SOCIETY

- Have their own, traditionally determined, internal set of rules and systems.
- Internalised norms of schools are different from those outside.

Universities

- Present themselves as élite establishments, a belief which is perpetuated by their hierarchies.
- The rules and regulations of universities are different from other mainstream education establishments.
- The norms of universities are totally separate from that of mainstream life.

Police

- The police enforce their own rules and these are different from society's, especially in terms of inquiries and disciplinary issues.
- They are well-known and recognised by all other members of society.
- Police quarters are distinctive and segregated.

Armed forces

- Established through tradition, *very* long standing.
- Armed forces have their own laws and punishments which are separate from those in legislated law (indeed an armed forces member can in some cases face two sets of punishment).
- Quarters readily identifiable and different.

Monasteries and convents

- Insular and established outside ordinary social boundaries.
- Easily recognised membership due to established traditions.
- Own set of rules and regulations not applicable to other members of society.

These are common examples of institutions with which we are all familiar, but there is one institution missing from the list that you will already be, or will become, very familiar with – the hospital. Hospitals, irrespective of the type or purpose, are all classic institutions, and until recently have perpetuated all the characteristics that are inherent to institutionalised environments.

Are asylums genuine havens of rest from the pressures of society or can they create even more gripping tensions in those already disturbed? How do mental patients adjust to their new life? And are their adjustments so very different from the reactions of members of other 'total institutions' such as Army camps, monasteries, prisons and boarding schools?   Back cover *Asylums* E GOFFMAN, 1961

We believe this book to be essential reading if you are attempting to understand the effects of an institution and its processes on the individual.

You may have noticed the use of the phrase 'total institutions' in the above quotation. What exactly did Goffman mean when he used this phrase? What is a 'total institution'? What are its characteristics?

Erving Goffman, in addition to his work on roles, as discussed earlier, published in 1968 a set of essays based on his observations of the inhabitants of, and their interactions within, Army camps, monasteries, prisons, boarding schools and mental hospitals. While he recognised the existence of differences, mainly those concerned with the establishments' functions, he also observed that all these establishments have 16 factors in common. Goffman suggests that when these 16 factors are present in one establishment then a 'total institution' exists.

Goffman's 16 Characteristics

1. All aspects of life are conducted in the same place, under the same single authority.
2. Each phase of activity is carried on in the company of others, all treated alike and required to do the same things together.
3. The day's activities are tightly scheduled with one activity leading to another at a pre-arranged time.
4. Sequencing of activities is imposed by a system of explicit formal rulings and a body of officials whose task is surveillance.
5. Various activities are brought together in a single rational plan designed to fulfil the official aims of the institution.
6. There is a basic split between a large managed group, the inmates, and a small supervisory group.
7. Each group tends to conceive of the other in terms of narrow, hostile types.
8. Staff tend to feel superior and righteous; inmates feel inferior, blameworthy and guilty.
9. Social mobility between the two groups is severely restricted; social distance is great and formally prescribed.
10. The passage of information about staff plans for inmates is restricted and inmates are excluded from decisions about their fate.
11. Incentives for work have little significance outside the institution.
12. Groups have only official points of contact.
13. There is a barrier between inmates and the outside world.
14. Inmates are de-possessed of basic rights.
15. High-ranking inmates have more authority than low-ranking supervisors.
16. Inmates are expected to internalise the norms of the staff.

Adapted from Goffman, 1968

 Take each of the 16 characteristics in turn and decide if they are present in the establishment where you work – give examples to illustrate how they exist. Also consider why these characteristics may be found in some establishments but not others.

Our responses in this case are based on our current working establishment, which happens to be a college of nursing and midwifery. Thus your examples may differ slightly in content but should not in the application of characteristics. We have outlined our responses to each of the 16 characteristics as related to our organisation.

Characteristic 1 The majority of the 'work' is conducted in one place, under the direct management of one organisational authority. 'Home' and 'leisure', however, are separate from work, a fact which may not be the case in a 'total institution' e.g. a prison. (If you 'live in' your work environment or college accommodation you might feel that work, home and leisure are not separated?) It might be argued by some that the Common Foundation Programme of P2000 reinforces this aspect of institutionalisation in that it emphasises 'sameness' as opposed to 'difference'.

Characteristic 2 Wherever *en masse* teaching takes place, the activities necessarily take place in the company of others and the larger the class the more alike each student is treated. Again, however, leisure and home activities are separated from this work process.

Characteristic 3 If college timetables are strictly adhered to then this point would also be applicable. Fortunately within our college there is some flexibility.

Characteristic 4 While the activities of the college are sequenced by 'formal rulings', e.g. the curriculum, there is flexibility, and while some students may argue that the tutor's role is surveillance, it is not!

Characteristic 5 In order to fulfil the official aims of the college, one of which could be said to be 'the supply of effective nurses', then a rational plan designed to achieve this is in fact desirable.

Characteristic 6 The 'inmates', i.e. the students of our college, may believe that a split exists between students and the teaching staff. While there are obvious differences between these two groups, an emphasis is however, placed on the 'equal' nature of the student/teacher relationship.

Characteristic 7 While the description 'narrow types' may be applied by either students or staff to the other group, we do not believe that these comments are overtly 'hostile' in nature.

Characteristic 8 The students and teachers may be able to cite examples of this sort of behaviour or at least a belief in its presence.

Characteristic 9 Within our college there are active attempts to integrate the two groups, e.g. through sporting activities. However, some students may still feel the effects of 'social distancing', both within the college and outside it when meeting members of the 'opposite' group in public places.

Characteristic 10 Participation in curriculum planning groups enables students to take part in the decision-making process, as do arenas such as joint tutorials. Some students, though, may still feel that their activities are heavily predetermined and that little choice is available.

Characteristic 11 Most colleges can be said to have assessment strategies which mean little outside the context of the course. The possession of a diploma at the end of the course, however, allows students to gain access to other educational opportunities. This then is an incentive that has relevance to others outside the college.

Characteristic 12 This is only partially true. There are official points of contact, e.g. tutorials in a tutor's 'office', but many unofficial contacts also exist.

Characteristic 13 Barriers are not formally prescribed as, for instance, they would be in a prison.

Characteristic 14 The college has no intention to restrict the basic rights of its students and acknowledges their rights within a students' charter.

Characteristic 15 Within the college the teachers clearly hold the positions of authority.

Characteristic 16 We could argue that the students are expected to adopt the educational 'norms' of the college, as well as 'nursing norms' expressed through the course curriculum. In contrast, though, they are not pressured to adopt the social or cultural norms of teachers.

It is evident from this brief examination of Goffman's findings that even the most liberal establishments can display, and even reinforce some of the traits, practices and kinds of behaviour that are present in a 'total institution'.

Rosabeth Moss Kanter (1990) further offers an insight into the effects of organisations when considering organisational variables which contribute to either power or powerlessness in individuals (see Table 4.2).

Power is generated when:

- There are few rules inherent to the job
- There have been few predecessors in the job
- There are few established routines
- There is a high task variety
- There are few rewards for reliability/predictability
- There are many rewards for unusual performance/innovation
- There is high flexibility in the use of people
- Few approvals are needed for non-routine decisions
- The physical location is central rather than distant
- Publicity about job activities is high
- The relation of tasks to current problems is central rather than peripheral
- The focus of tasks is outside the work unit
- There is high interpersonal contact in the job
- Contact with senior officials is high
- There is high participation in programmes, conferences and meetings
- Participation in problem-solving task forces is high
- The advancement prospects for junior personnel are high

The opposite categories when present will lead to powerlessness in the individual

Table 4.2. Power generation.

While Kanter's primary concern was with illustrating the means of giving power to the employees of an organisation, many of her factors are also pertinent to the empowerment of client/patient groups. Further on in this chapter we shall discuss staff who work within institutional settings, and it is worth while taking a minute or two to reflect upon the following comment on staff attitudes.

> *Staff remain in one place for a variable length of time, and the institution may retain for longer periods those members whose attitudes are in conformity with the prevailing ideology [of the institution].*

HALL, 1982

It is all too easy to become 'stuck in a rut', to accept what is going on, and to conform without question – to become institutionalised! The next part of this chapter will examine the characteristics of institutional life for, to use Goffman's labels, both inmates and staff.

If you begin to recognise yourselves in these pages, then it is time for you to re-assess your position, status and purpose in life, and more importantly to assess your potential and your attitude towards your future careers. If conformity is allowed to become a 'norm', and acceptance of all things becomes standard practice, then a progressive and proactive service for your service users can never be realised.

Institutionalisation

Goffman describes the effect of institutional life on both inmates and staff and how the dominance of the institution's norms, atmosphere and perhaps above all, its purpose, begins to influence and eventually dominate the lives of these people. Within the 'total institution' all aspects of everyday living take place within the boundaries and parameters that are established by the authorities that manage the institution in question. Wing cites the work of Bettelheim and Sylvester, who in 1948 described:

> . . . *an institution in which a rigid, comprehensive and impersonal regime allowed no scope for individual decisions on the part of the inmate children and demanding only their compliance, led to emotional apathy, lack of spontaneity, and an incapacity for active adjustment to events which were commonplace to non-institutionalised children.*
>
> WING, 1962

In the 1958 study entitled *The Hospital and its Patients*, Titmuss indicated that the same tendencies occurred in some general hospitals and Wing notes Titmuss stating (in 1959) that:

> . . . *for most people institutional life has spelt little besides ugliness, cheapness, and restricted liberties.*
>
> WING, 1962

Aspects of everyday living within the institution include many of the activities we frequently take for granted as being basic rights, based on the principles of *freedom of choice* and *opportunity*.

Life in an Institution

 Just for five minutes reflect on the things that *you* take for granted in your life.

The things that the authors take for granted may well be similar to your own. This is an important consideration when examining life in an institution as the things that we take for granted are a reflection of our right, and opportunity, to make choices. The authors' answers to this exercise, given below, are related to those needs and desires which are common to all human beings. We tend to take for granted our right to meet these needs and desires but not all humans have the same opportunities, nor the freedom of choice to do so . . .

1 To eat what we want to eat – within reason and affordability!

2 To read what we want to read – irrespective of the views or opinions of others.

3 To write to whom we wish, when we wish to.

4 To associate with whom we want – and to dissociate ourselves from those we do not want to be with.

5 When applicable, for example during holidays, to go to bed when we wish, and to get up when we want to.

6 To enter into discussion/debates/arguments with people on a variety of topics, e.g. politics, sport, musical taste, and what to eat at dinner!

7 To wear the clothes that we want to wear.

8 To smoke (or not to smoke), to drink (or not to drink).

9 To visit friends, relatives, and neighbours when we choose to.

10 To spend our money on what we wish (within reason!).

 **Important Note**: For these examples and your own, it is important to remember that we are examining life in what is, by comparison to others, a liberal society. Other countries and cultures will have different perspectives on *freedom, choice,* and *opportunity*.

We are therefore noting that in a 'liberal' society individuals tend to have a wider choice than those in more restrictive countries. At this point it is necessary to say that even in the United Kingdom it could be argued that freedom and choice are limited depending on mobility, wealth, health and motivation, but the effects of an institution are relative to all societies, i.e. the institution will suppress those freedoms that exist *outside* its boundaries for the inmates *inside* the boundaries, although the severity of this suppression will vary between differing institutions.

The importance of freedom of choice to the making of an 'institutional climate' is clearly identified by Hall (1982) who, when comparing institutions within his own studies, states:

> *A key idea linking these studies is that of clients' decision-making freedom.*

Hall also lists 21 of the most common, and for us, perhaps the most taken for granted, decision-making freedoms we have in everyday life. Before spending time giving thought to Hall's list, it is worth pondering on the following quotation from his book:

'Whether an institution allows this exercise of choice to continue for its clients or whether these decision-making freedoms are curtailed is crucial in determining whether an institution creates a therapeutic climate – or institutionalisation.'

HALL, J. *(1982)*, *Psychology for Nurses and Health Visitors*, Basingstoke: Macmillan Education, *p. 318.*

We do recommend that you, as service-providers, become familiar with this book.

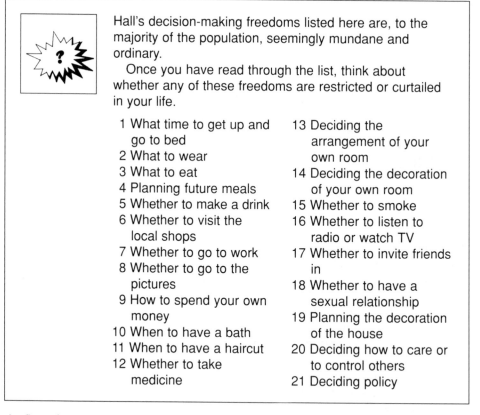

Hall's decision-making freedoms listed here are, to the majority of the population, seemingly mundane and ordinary.

Once you have read through the list, think about whether any of these freedoms are restricted or curtailed in your life.

1 What time to get up and go to bed
2 What to wear
3 What to eat
4 Planning future meals
5 Whether to make a drink
6 Whether to visit the local shops
7 Whether to go to work
8 Whether to go to the pictures
9 How to spend your own money
10 When to have a bath
11 When to have a haircut
12 Whether to take medicine
13 Deciding the arrangement of your own room
14 Deciding the decoration of your own room
15 Whether to smoke
16 Whether to listen to radio or watch TV
17 Whether to invite friends in
18 Whether to have a sexual relationship
19 Planning the decoration of the house
20 Deciding how to care or to control others
21 Deciding policy

At first glance, we might suggest that we do not have any restrictions placed on these decisions, but on closer inspection we begin to notice that even outside an institution, freedoms are not as straightforward as we would like to think. There are subtle social and cultural pressures which affect the use of these decision-making freedoms.

If we accept Goffman's, Wing's and Titmuss's accounts of an institution-orientated existence, it is reasonable to suggest that wherever institutional practices occur then the characteristics of that institution will be present in both the people who live there *and* those who work within it. When a person displays these characteristics they are solely reliant and dependent both on the system and other individuals for their existence. These people are said to be *institutionalised.*

 Using your knowledge of Goffman and your own experiences of an institution, your present situation included, list the factors that result in the process of institutionalisation.

Think about the following factors particularly and how they influence the process.

- Staff

- Policies

- Clients/patients

- Historical influences

We have outlined below some of those factors which we believe may be relevant to the process of institutionalisation:

Staff – Age; when and how trained (affects attitude to care); personality; how long in post; position in system; gender.

Policy – How practical; how rigid; how flexible; how realistic (especially regarding sexual relationships, employment, etc); how restrictive (especially for individual development).

Clients – Age; how long in the institution; personality; individual abilities and insights; peer group pressure to conform.

History – Stigma attached to institutions; historical use; society's belief in institution's usefulness; social acceptance of people being in the institution.

Some institutions have survived by reinforcing the institutionalisation process. For example, the armed forces perpetuate policies that both identify and divide the numerous ranks e.g.

Aircraftman – Leading Aircraftman – Corporal – Sergeant – Flight Sergeant – Warrant Officer

Each of these ranks in the RAF has power and authority over those directly below them in the hierarchy. History has made the armed forces, and thus their hierarchies of division, acceptable to society, and the same principle can be applied to the examples of institutions given previously.

Martin (1974) describes the historical style of institutional care and its effects on the individual as a custodial practice, the efficiency of which was measured in terms of orderliness and tidiness. The therapeutic relationship between patient and nurse was of less importance. Approaches relying on authority and submission maintained this state of affairs. Authoritarian approaches generated feelings of powerlessness and resentment in the client/patient in addition to robbing them of initiative, responsibility and the ability to make decisions. Effective channels for emotional release were absent and this combined with repressive approaches led to many symptoms reminiscent of mental illness. These symptoms included challenging behaviours and self-isolation and the demands of such regimes led to chronic problems and institutionalised individuals.

Martin's book *Adventure in Psychiatry* details the life of the individuals residing in Claybury Hospital (a large mental institution in Greater London) and the attempts of the staff of the hospital to introduce a more positive existence for their patients. It details well the history of the institution and the first moves that were being made towards the 'community ethos' that permeates contemporary mental health services. It is well worth a browse.

MARTIN, D. (1974) *Adventure in Psychiatry.*
Oxford: Bruno Cassirer.

The four elements of staff, policy, clients/patients and history serve not only to ensure the continued existence of institutions, but also to maintain a fifth element necessary for the survival of institutions – **conformity**.

Having examined the wider processes of institutionalisation, it becomes important to examine the effects that an institutional existence has on the lives of the people who live within the institution.

> *The quality of institutions varies greatly, but a frequent reaction is one of withdrawal, depression, and depersonalisation. Despite having many people around, the old person may suffer from a deep sense of loneliness and isolation . . .*

HALL, 1982.

Although this quotation specifically cites the example of an elderly person, it is wholly appropriate to all individuals who are admitted into an institution – caring ones or otherwise.

When the admission becomes a long-term period of care, then the individual may display extreme effects as a result of the institutional processes to which they become subject. These processes, for example, may effect their personality, attitude, physical presentation and ability.

THE INDIVIDUAL IN SOCIETY

Using the quotation from Hall above as a starting-point, describe how an institutionalised individual may appear to someone who is unaware of their way of life.

How does your description compare to ours?

- Apathetic
- Lacking initiative
- Lacking interest in all but the mundane
- Submissive to authority
- Unable to make decisions
- Reluctant to deviate from set routine
- Vacant or absent expression
- Stooped gait
- Little or no interest in personal appearance
- Unable to initiate action
- Difficulty in maintaining or forming meaningful relationships.
- Ineffective in performing the simplest of everyday tasks

The presence of such characteristics in the individual are believed by some to be indicative of a disease which is described by Barton under the name of institutional neurosis:

> . . . a disease characterised by apathy, lack of initiative, loss of interest, especially in things of an impersonal nature, submissiveness, apparent inability to make plans for the future, lack of individuality, and sometimes a characteristic posture and gait.
>
> BARTON, 1976

Barton believes therefore that institutionalisation can be viewed as an illness whose treatment is change in the hospital environment or exit from it. The characteristics of the individual described above are closely related to restricted opportunities to make decisions for themselves. There are numerous reasons why these decisions are taken away from the inmate population. Frequently the reasons revolve around two aspects of institutional life:

1 Staff autonomy

2 Inmate dependency

Because the inmate population is, generally, large and the staff numbers are comparatively small, all aspects of living are conducted *en masse*, as this ensures the most economical utilisation of the staff, while still providing for the basic needs of the inmates.

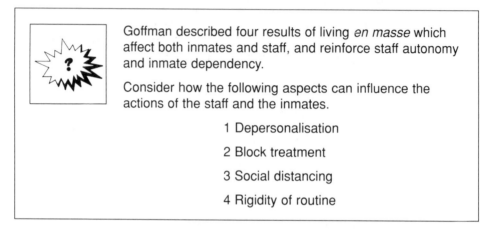

Goffman described four results of living *en masse* which affect both inmates and staff, and reinforce staff autonomy and inmate dependency.

Consider how the following aspects can influence the actions of the staff and the inmates.

1 Depersonalisation

2 Block treatment

3 Social distancing

4 Rigidity of routine

Note: These suggestions are not only based on Goffman's observation, but are also drawn from first-hand experience.

1 Individuals (staff/clients/patients) become stereotyped, because everyday activities and experiences are standardised, e.g. similar clothing, identical furnishings, etc. Clients/patients have little chance to express individuality or explore their own preferences and therefore development rarely occurs.

2 Everyday, mundane tasks are carried out *en masse*, especially at busy times – e.g. dinner, bath-time, etc. All activities are carried out in the presence of others. Staff have little opportunity to give individual attention to clients/patients, and opportunities for teaching are therefore minimised.

3 Interactions between clients/patients and staff are rarely on an equal basis. For example, staff will frequently *tell* a client/patient what to do, and not do, but a client/patient will not make suggestions to staff. Social activities such as eating and drinking are segregated, with staff eating separately from their client groups.

4 The very existence of many institutions is based on fixed

THE INDIVIDUAL IN SOCIETY

routines. Dressing, eating, bathing, visiting, etc. will take place each day, each week, at the same time, in the same place, and be performed by the same people.

In addition Barton identifies the following factors as being an aetiology for the 'illness':

1 Loss of contact with the outside world.

2 Enforced idleness and loss of responsibility.

3 Brutality, browbeating and teasing (by staff).

4 Bossiness of professional staff.

5 Loss of personal friends, possessions and personal events.

6 Heavy use of drugs.

7 Repressive ward atmosphere.

8 Loss of prospects outside the institution.

In Whose Best Interest?

Institutions have, over the years, gained reputations that do little to enhance the image of an establishment that provides care and/or protection. In recent years many questions have been asked regarding all forms of institutions – prisons, the armed forces, the police, hospitals (all types), and even nursing colleges! And one question is always asked:

Whose Interests are Best Served by Institutions?

What follows is a condensed account of one person's attempts to break out of the institutional mould. It is taken from the Open University course *P555, Mental Handicap: Patterns for Living* (Open University, 1987). Although this is concerned with John, a person with learning disabilities, it could very easily apply to anyone wishing to leave the confines of an institutional setting.

John has lived in a long-stay hospital for 27 years, and he is now into his 40s. At a recent care review John, quite unexpectedly, stated that he wanted to 'live outside'. After the initial shock the professionals present, including nurses, began giving a series of responses that suggest that John could not survive 'outside':

'He doesn't understand what it's like out there'
'History of aggressive outbursts'
'He'd miss the company'
'He's too dependent'
'He'd miss the entertainment'
'Better off here – no worries, no responsibilities'
'Too institutionalised'
'People would take advantage of him'

'Too handicapped – can't talk'
'He'd be isolated and lonely'
'He'd forget to take his drugs'
'No family support'
'He couldn't manage without us'
'He might fail'
'He needs care and protection'
'Too big a risk'
'He needs treatment'

While seeming quite plausible, all these reasons for not allowing John the chance are based quite simply on the fact that he has spent 27 years in an institution. Those who have made these statements are probably concerned with what they would argue as being 'John's best interests', and undoubtedly, they care about John's future.

But . . .

In recent years the philosophies that have reinforced the patterns of institutional care have been surpassed and almost literally, 'turned around'. Many of the classic hospital institutions within the United Kingdom, either are now preparing their populations for a place in the community or have largely completed this process.

Institutions such as prisons, monasteries, convents, special hospitals (e.g. Rampton, Broadmoor, Carstairs), and mental health hospitals now openly encourage programmes of integration for inmates capable of sustaining an acceptable standard of social integration. Even within general hospital services, greater emphasis is placed upon the care of patients prior to admission and to the care given after discharge and to the maintenance of individuals within the community in which they live.

However, the most dramatic changes have taken place within the services that are provided for people with learning disabilities. In less than 13 years, since the publication of the report of the committee of inquiry into mental handicap, nursing and care (the Jay Report 1979) the large hospitals for these people have been greatly reduced and the inmate populations have been reintroduced to an active existence in the community. These changes have occurred for many reasons, too many to be documented here, but the most influential one has been the power of positive thought . . .

Positive Thought

To return to John's example, each of the professionals who made the negative comments should have looked at John's strengths – and this applies to any client/patient, irrespective of his or her ability or disability, illness or well-being. In John's case the following comments could have been made – after all, when a client shows a positive initiative, i.e. 'I want to live in the community,' then surely he deserves an encouraging and positive response?

'Highly motivated'
'Pleasant person'
'No longer aggressive'
'Well liked'
'Still a young man'
'He'd benefit from a stimulating environment'
'No trouble'
'Understands what's going on'
'His epilepsy is under control these days'
'Says a few words'
'Would enjoy a new life-style'
'Has adapted to change all right in the past'
'Free agent – no family ties'
'Deserves a change after 27 years'

The Final Point

The final point in the story of institutions and institutionalisation concerns you and your colleagues i.e. future service providers.

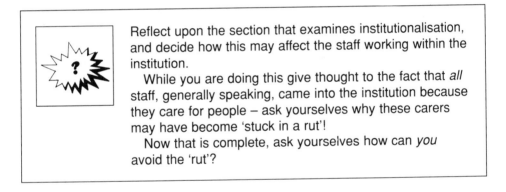

Reflect upon the section that examines institutionalisation, and decide how this may affect the staff working within the institution.

While you are doing this give thought to the fact that *all* staff, generally speaking, came into the institution because they care for people – ask yourselves why these carers may have become 'stuck in a rut'!

Now that is complete, ask yourselves how can *you* avoid the 'rut'?

In *Hospitals in Trouble* (a vivid account of the problems of institutions) Martin (1984) describes the work of Sykes and Matza which suggests how people with the duty of caring for others can actually ill-treat them. Sykes and Matza consider this issue using a number of described 'techniques of neutralisation':

1 'The denial of injury' – this technique of neutralisation is held to be particularly relevant to the elderly and people with a learning disability. The action of the carer is rationalised on the basis that the victim does not understand, or feel, and therefore does not suffer.

2 'The denial of the victim' – the labelling of the victim as disruptive or challenging or ungrateful seeks to justify ill-treatment as something deserved (you will remember thinking about the effects of labelling in Chapter 3).

3 'The denial of responsibility' – the carer rationalises that forces outside his or her control cause ill-treatment, e.g. stress, overwork, low-staffing, 'acting under orders'. Thus the nurse's/midwife's individual responsibility/accountability is neatly rendered unimportant.

4 'Condemnation of the condemners' – the condemning of 'do-gooders' as not really understanding or for being hypocritical or for being motivated by personal spite. This technique assumes that condemners condemn because they do not possess 'true knowledge' and are therefore 'ignorant'. Martin refers to this ploy as 'the defence of professional mystification'. This technique of neutralisation, though, has two inherent weaknesses:

   i It simply deflects criticism and does not address the issue.

   ii It makes the assumption that professional knowledge and action are unquestionably 'right'. The history of care practices in the UK and their effects on people would suggest otherwise in many instances.

5 'Appeal to higher loyalties' – the attitudes of colleagues prescribe norms of behaviour through loyalty to the staff group. This can lead to, at best, conservative and restrictive approaches to care and at worst to long-term physical and emotional abuse. Additionally change-agents may experience severe pressures to conform to the 'agreed norm'.

Sykes and Matza suggest that techniques of neutralisation can be used to enable trained staff to rationalise behaviour which they must recognise as wrong. In this way staff may perpetuate institutional practices and allow themselves to become 'stuck in a rut'. There are a number of ways in which you can avoid this and also avoid placing your patients/clients in a 'rut' of their own:

- Treat all patients/clients as individuals.

- Avoid the use of stigmatising labels.

- Encourage patients/clients to make *choices*.

- Provide *opportunities* for patients/clients to make choices, to learn and to participate as fully as possible in the planning of their future care.

- Allow access to non-institutional facilities.

- Involve yourself in staff development which includes courses on contemporary developments in nursing/midwifery, particularly those developments relevant to your speciality and patient/client group.

- Encourage the development of patient/client independence.

- Prompt staff to express themselves and provide an environment within which they feel 'safe' to do so.

- Identify support systems that may be available for yourself and other staff members, and make these known to all who may benefit from their use.

- Encourage parent/guardian/next-of-kin participation in care planning and delivery.

- Within 'long-stay' facilities try to create a 'homely' environment, one that mirrors positive living standards elsewhere in the local community.

- Work at creating a relaxed, friendly atmosphere.

- Prompt patients/clients to make *decisions* for themselves.

- Reduce as far as possible the use of institutional signs and symbols, e.g. uniforms, nameplates, badges and notices.

- Develop advocacy and self-advocacy systems wherever necessary.

- Represent the interests of your patients/clients in a positive manner to others.

- Seek to enhance the 'public image' of your patients/clients and your organisation.

- Involve yourself in induction courses for new staff which promote the rights/needs of your patients/clients together with the contemporary means of meeting these rights and needs.

- Reduce the emphasis on hierarchical status and focus on the team nature of your work and the best use of all available skills.

- Emphasise the 'equal' nature of the relationship between staff and clients/patients.

- Ensure that you, and other staff, are aware of your/their responsibilities with regard to professional development.

- Try to base practice on proven research which enhances the quality of care and quality of life.

- Reduce barriers between staff and patients/clients which encourage social distancing, e.g. rooms designated for the use of one group which could easily be shared by the other.

- Use postal addresses for long-stay facilities which identify their presence in the local community rather than site names which associate them with the service providing the facility.

- Allocate long-stay facilities a separate telephone line rather than communicating to them via a main switchboard. This again gives the facility an identity of its own in the local community.

Barton, writing in 1976, recommended the adoption of a number of principles within long-term care institutions which are now accepted as the norm:

- establishing contact with the family and community

- providing meaningful activities for patients/clients

- looking to attitude change in staff

- encouraging friendships

- encouraging the presence of personal possessions and recognition of personal events

- reducing the use of medication

- the providing of a homely environment

- orientating of patients/clients to life outside the hospital

- the eradicating of authoritarian or controlling staff management.

Without doubt there are numerous other innovative actions or approaches which might be taken to avoid the 'rut', both for yourself and for your patients/clients, some of which you may well have already identified. The important point to remember, though, is that we all should take time to reflect upon, and evaluate critically, our actions and also check the results of this process against the perceptions of others. That is, we should clarify our perceptions of our actions against an external objective appraisal.

Conclusions

Institutions were originally devised in order to provide care, safety and protection. In the beginning these establishments provided for the basic needs of many unwanted (by society) and unloved (by relatives) people. In time *society* began to forget about the people inside the institutions. Society forgot the inmates, it forgot the staff, and consequently the institutions developed their own rules and regulations and their own 'legal' systems that were not those applied to other citizens. Society is now having to accept that institutions do exist, and that their populations have a right to be reintegrated into the community.

This process of acceptance will take time, but we have now got the time and the opportunities to change the characteristics that perpetuate the image conjured up by the word 'institution'. The main element in this change is *you*; *your* attitudes and behaviour; but above all, *your* interactions with, and acceptance and promotion of, the people you care for.

References

Barton R (1976) *Institutional Neurosis*, 3rd edn. Bristol: John Wright and Sons.

Collins Contemporary Dictionary (1984) London: Collins.

Emerson R W (1993) In Andrews R (ed) The Columbia Dictionary of Quotations. New York: Columbia University Press.

Etzioni A (1961) *Complex Organisations*. New York: Holt, Rinehart and Winston.

Fowler H W and Fowler F G (1967) *The Concise Oxford Dictionary*, 5th edn. Oxford: Oxford University Press.

Getzels J W (1958) Administration as a Social Process. In: Halpin A W, *Administrative Theory in Education*. Chicago: University of Chicago.

Goffman E (1968) *Asylums: An Essay on the Social Situation of Mental Patients and Other Inmates*. Harmondsworth: Pelican.

Hall J (1982) *Psychology for Nurses and Health Visitors*. Basingstoke: Macmillan Education.

Herriot P (1976) *Essential Psychology – Culture's Influence on Behaviour*. London: Methuen.

Kanter R M (1990) Power Failure in Management Circuits. In: Pugh D S (ed) *Organisation Theory – Selected Readings*, 3rd edn. Harmondsworth: Penguin.

Krech D, Crutchfield R S and Ballachey E L (1962) *Individual in Society – A Textbook of Social Psychology*. London: McGraw Hill.

Lindzey G and Aronson E (1969) *The Handbook of Social Psychology*, 2nd edn. London: Addison-Wesley.

Martin D (1974) *Adventure in Psychiatry*. Oxford: Bruno Cassirer.

Martin J (1984) *Hospitals in Trouble*. Oxford: Basil Blackwell.

National Health Service and Community Care Act (1990). London: HMSO.

Open Systems Group (1987) *Systems Behaviour*, 3rd edn. London: Paul Chapman.

Open University (1986) *Social Sciences: a Foundation Course. Block 5: Conformity, Consensus and Conflict*. Milton Keynes: Open University Press.

Open University (1987) *P555 – Mental Handicap: Patterns for Living*. Milton Keynes: Open University Press.

Paton R, Brown S, Spear R, Chapman J, Floyd M and Hamwee J (1987) *Organisations: Cases, Issues, Concepts*. London: Harper and Row.

Potter D and Anderson J (1981) *Society and the Social Sciences*. London: Routledge and Kegan Paul.

Report of the Committee of Enquiry into Mental Handicap Nursing and Care (1979) The Jay Report. London: HMSO.

Shils E (1975) Centre and periphery. In: Potter D (1981) *Society and the Social Sciences: An Introduction*. London: Routledge and Kegan Paul.

Thompson L F, Miller M H and Bigler H F (1975) *Sociology – Nurses and their Patients in a Modern Society*, 9th edn. Saint Louis: C V Mosby.

Titmuss R M (1958) *The Hospital and its Patients: Essays on the Welfare State*. London: Allen and Unwin.

Titmuss R M (1959) Community care as a challenge. *The Times*, 12 May.

White W (1986) In: Pugh D S, Hickson D J and Hinings C R (1986) *Writers on Organisations*, 3rd edn. Harmondsworth: Penguin Books.

Wing J K (1967) Institutionalism in Mental Hospitals. In: Scheff T J (ed) *Mental Illness and Social Processes*. London: Harper and Row.

CHAPTER 5

Communication and Caring

If there is one general law of communication it is that we never communicate as effectively as we think we do.

CHARLES HANDY

5 Communication and Caring

In order to get any truth about myself, I must have contact with another person. The other is indispensable to my own experience, as well as to my knowledge about myself . . .

JEAN-PAUL SARTRE

Introduction

Irrespective of ability or disability, race or culture, well-being or ill-health, everyone communicates. Communication is a necessity fundamental to our existence. Without some form of communication human beings could not develop, nor could we manipulate the world in which we live:

Man is a social animal: he collaborates with others to pursue his goals and satisfy his needs . . .

ARGYLE, 1983

A major goal of the individual is a desire for well-being, and each of us pursues this desire in different ways. Occasionally we find ourselves unable or unwilling, for whatever reason, to continue the pursuit alone. Whether we are able to continue alone, or require assistance in acquiring well-being, it is paramount that we are capable of communicating with other individuals in such a manner that the messages being conveyed are understood by the recipients. When an individual's well-being has been undermined in some way and in addition there are manifest problems with communication, it may become necessary to make use of an interpreter: a person who can interpret and convey the messages being sent, so that the desire for well-being is still met.

That interpreter may well be *you*, the client's/patient's advocate or named nurse. This role places great responsibility in your hands; more accurately, it places emphasis on your ability to receive and translate the client's/patient's message and to transmit your response in a manner which enables the client/patient to understand.

Whichever specialty you adopt in the future, be it learning disability, adult, mental health or child nursing or midwifery, you will need to collaborate with people to enable them to pursue their goals and needs. Before collaboration can take place you must first understand and develop your own communication systems and strategies. The principles apply equally to the communications we enter into with other members of the care team. Without communication care could not take place. Therefore, effective personal communication is essential for effective care delivery.

This chapter will ask you to examine many aspects of your own communication. It will also ask you to assess whether your methods are effective, although it must be stressed that the real test of effective communication takes place during the interactions you have with the people you care for.

Objectives

Having studied Chapter 5 you should be able to:

1 Define **communication**.

2 Compare and contrast the **linear**, **interactive** and **transactional models** of communication.

3 Describe communication concepts such as **sender, encode, message, channel, decode, receiver** and **noise**.

4 Discuss the reasons for communicating and what people achieve via communication.

5 Outline the **'four needs of communication'**.

6 Discuss the differences in communication resulting from **illness, disablement** or a **disadvantaged life-style**.

7 Outline the effect of **self-concept** on communication.

8 Describe the key components of **verbal** and **non-verbal** communication.

9 Explain the use of **body language** and **symbolic representation** as means of non-verbal communication.

10 Apply your learning about communication to achieve **effectiveness** as a **practitioner**.

What is communication?

> *A word is not a bird: once on the wing, it cannot be caught again . . .*
>
> RUSSIAN PROVERB

In the introduction to this chapter it has been argued that it is impossible to be healthy without having some means by which to communicate. It is equally important to say that without communication the capability to care effectively is also impossible. Holistic care cannot thrive in an environment deprived of communication. But what is communication? What are its ingredients? And what are the processes that facilitate communication? In an attempt to answer these questions you will be asked to examine what is, for most of us, such a commonplace phenomenon that we take it for granted . . . after all, we all communicate, don't we?

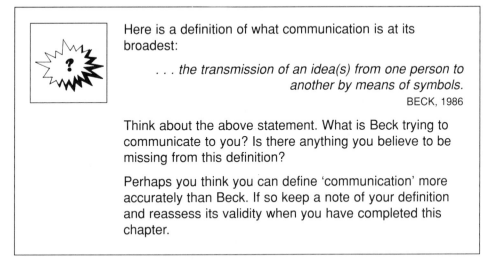

Here is a definition of what communication is at its broadest:

> *. . . the transmission of an idea(s) from one person to another by means of symbols.*
>
> BECK, 1986

Think about the above statement. What is Beck trying to communicate to you? Is there anything you believe to be missing from this definition?

Perhaps you think you can define 'communication' more accurately than Beck. If so keep a note of your definition and reassess its validity when you have completed this chapter.

Despite its apparent simplicity Beck's statement provides an invaluable insight into the complexities of communication. For communication to exist, an individual must first have some ideas, thoughts, notions or messages that they wish to send (transmit) to another person, using some form of symbolic representation.

Communication now becomes a more complex issue. If individuals wish to pass on their ideas they must use symbols . . . What symbols? Do symbols exist for all the ideas you want to send? If so which are the most suitable?

The Linear Model

Unfortunately, Beck seemingly refers only to one-way communication – one to another – and thus provides only part of the answer. Beck's definition is based on a *linear model* of communication. Figure 5.1 is a diagrammatic representation of the linear model and illustrates the components of the communication process.

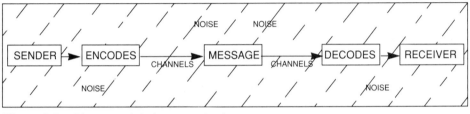

Figure 5.1. Linear model of communication

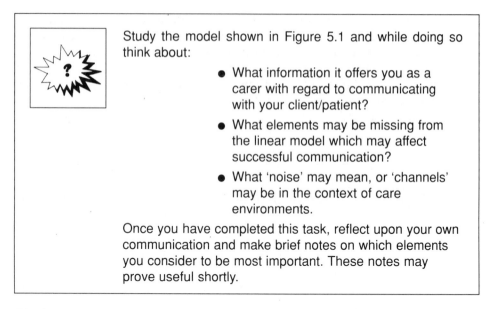

Study the model shown in Figure 5.1 and while doing so think about:

- What information it offers you as a carer with regard to communicating with your client/patient?
- What elements may be missing from the linear model which may affect successful communication?
- What 'noise' may mean, or 'channels' may be in the context of care environments.

Once you have completed this task, reflect upon your own communication and make brief notes on which elements you consider to be most important. These notes may prove useful shortly.

The following elements are considered to be of importance to effective communication.

1 The sender's encoding of a message is important. The manner in which they code the message to be sent will also have a bearing on the channel used. What you understand as a carer may not be understood in the same way by those you are caring for, e.g. imagine how *you* would feel if a nurse/midwife was to tell you that you were going to 'have a PR' and you did not understand what a PR examination entailed . . . until it was delivered, per rectum! A shared perception of the language being used is crucial.

The need for shared perceptions will affect the channels used. Do you use verbal or non-verbal channels? Spoken or written word? What form of symbolic representation will be most effective? Computer users will be only too familiar with the frustration of trying to transfer information from one system to another when they do not share a common language! The channels used will affect the receiver's ability to understand and subsequently act upon the sender's messages, and when the sender's role is concerned with enabling people to become autonomous, it is paramount that messages are sent through the most appropriate channels.

How would a Community Mental Handicap Nurse (CMHN) make an approach to a new referral? Would he or she telephone first? Or write a letter? Or maybe call round in person? Each channel has its own strengths and weaknesses related to the context of the referral. When using channels give some thought to the strengths and weaknesses – could you use a more effective channel?

2 Perhaps the single most important element this model fails to represent is **understanding**. It is essential that **both** the sender and receiver understand the message.

For example, what if the nurse/midwife performing the rectal examination were to tell the patient that he or she was 'going to have an examination per rectum' and the patient responded with 'What's per rectum, nurse?' Does the nurse/midwife describe the rectum in detail? Does the rectum become an 'anal cavity'? ('What's an anal cavity, nurse?') What matters is the patient's need to understand the procedure and your ability to meet this need via the appropriate communication of information.

Very little communication is only one-way, and even that which may be considered so (e.g. a media broadcast) often stimulates people into discussing the issues raised or, if the topic is emotive enough, may even motivate action.

Modern technology facilitates communication without personal contact; for example, automatic cash dispensers have removed the need to interact personally with the bank teller. The communications you enter into, however, are still invariably interpersonal; this involves, for example, interaction between the client/patient and yourself. This interactive process is also present within the effective multidisciplinary team.

The interactive communication model is discussed next, but first there follows a brief explanation of the terminology used in the linear model.

Noise – At its simplest, 'noise' refers to any interference that occurs in the communication process. The intensity of this noise will affect the elements of the process, e.g. interference on a telephone line or distraction while talking to a patient or client.

Channel(s) – These are the modes by which your messages are conveyed – speech, the written word, sign language and care plans being examples.

Encoding – Translating ideas, thoughts and messages into a form which can be understood by the recipient and which is appropriate for the channel being used. For example, telephone communication involves encoding human speech into digital code which can be transmitted through electrical impulses. The recipient's telephone then decodes the digital message and converts it back to human speech.

The Interactive Model

Figure 5.2 is a diagrammatic representation of the *interactive model of communication*. All forms of communication can be considered to be interactive, including reading, watching television, conversing and so on, and this model of communication may be considered the most appropriate. This supposition should be easier for you to consider after the further examination of this model.

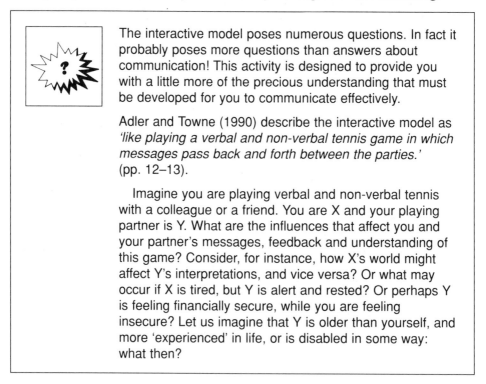

Figure 5.2. Interactive model of communication

A comparison of the two models illustrates the cyclic nature of the interactive model which differs from the nature of the linear model. There is also the added dimension of feedback, a prime need in your interactions with clients/patients. The quality of the feedback is determined by the degree of understanding.

The interactive model poses numerous questions. In fact it probably poses more questions than answers about communication! This activity is designed to provide you with a little more of the precious understanding that must be developed for you to communicate effectively.

Adler and Towne (1990) describe the interactive model as *'like playing a verbal and non-verbal tennis game in which messages pass back and forth between the parties.'* (pp. 12–13).

Imagine you are playing verbal and non-verbal tennis with a colleague or a friend. You are X and your playing partner is Y. What are the influences that affect you and your partner's messages, feedback and understanding of this game? Consider, for instance, how X's world might affect Y's interpretations, and vice versa? Or what may occur if X is tired, but Y is alert and rested? Or perhaps Y is feeling financially secure, while you are feeling insecure? Let us imagine that Y is older than yourself, and more 'experienced' in life, or is disabled in some way: what then?

You will probably have realised that the first difficulty encountered with this model is that no two people share the same 'world'; each of us has a different perception of the environment in which we live. Our experiences are also unique – the way we are brought up by our parents, our education; these together with our personal beliefs combine with other factors to make 'our world' an individual existence.

Although our experiences are different, you will have noted that the model displays an area of overlap. This overlap reflects those experiences that the two

---

'That word was in'

players have in common. The size of this overlap is largely dependent on the message being communicated and is therefore variable. Your ability as carers to acquire as much background about a person as is possible will enhance the overlap, and thus the understanding. Later in this chapter strategies and skills will be outlined which will enable you and your clients/patients to share more of the same world.

Another important factor is the individual 'noise' that each player brings to the game. This can be physical, psychological, environmental, social, spiritual or emotional. Each player's noise will affect not only themselves, but also the other player. It may be a worthwhile diversion to take five minutes now to list the noise that is currently influencing your interactions with this text . . . your list may surprise you. You may have also noted that despite consideration of feedback and the individuals' worlds the interactive model is not flawless. For instance it is static, having defined beginnings and endings; and it is assumed that the sender's message causes some effect upon the receiver. These characteristics, as you may know from experience, are not always found in the 'real' communication process.

The Transactional Model

When you are seeking an appropriate model of communication to apply to the caring process the *transactional model* is well worth considering. It may also enable you to 'share the world' of all the people you will have contact with during your life. The following quotation ably states the reasons for considering a transactional model in the care process:

. . . the most important feature of nursing is seen to be the interpersonal transaction. Nursing is seen as something occurring between two people . . . Nursing is not carried out on a patient but with him . . .

FRENCH, 1989

Although specifically referring to nursing, the quotation is equally applicable to all health care personnel. French goes on to use a definition of 'transactional' as follows:

Relating to negotiating, conducting, performing, or carrying on, as an act or process; pertaining to an interplay.

FRENCH, 1989

Figure 5.3 illustrates the transactional model.

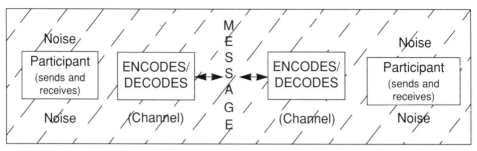

Figure 5.3.   The transactional model of communication

Examine the transactional communication model shown in Figure 5.3 and determine how it differs from the two previous models illustrated in this chapter. While thinking about these differences also make notes on what advantages the transactional view may have if applied to the process of providing care.

The first important point is that this model recognises the need for participation. The participants send and receive messages simultaneously. This means that each person's 'world' becomes interactive and in turn this should facilitate greater understanding. Another major difference is that the transactional model is not static. It constantly alters according to on-going interactions. At any given moment we are capable of receiving, decoding and responding (transmitting) to, another person's actions, while the other person is also receiving, decoding and responding. For instance, let us consider the following conversation and its outcome; as soon as you speak (send) they begin to hear (receive):

Carer: 'I'd like to talk about your current care-plan again.'

Patient/client: Frowns noticeably (responds) before speaking.

Carer: Receives frown, and sighs deeply (responds) and says 'Do I understand that you do not want to discuss this?'

Patient/client: Hears the sigh, ignores the words and lets the carer continue . . .

This situation illustrates how interactions can become misinterpreted if you are unaware of the communication processes that are involved. Using the transactional view the effective communicator might have interpreted the message to mean that:

- The patient/client did not want to discuss his or her care-plan, but would have also responded positively to explorations of the reason why, or

- Did not understand what was being asked – the frown indicating puzzlement rather than resistance.

You can now conclude this section by redefining in your own words what communication is.

If your definition is similar to the following then you are on course to understanding the transactional nature of communication and caring.

Communication is a continuous, transactional process involving participants who occupy different but overlapping environments and create a relationship by simultaneously sending and receiving messages, many of which are distorted by physical and psychological noise.

ADLER AND TOWNE, 1990

The next section explores the process of communication further and seeks to provide strategies which will enable your patients/clients to increase their own understanding of the caring process.

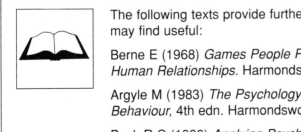

The following texts provide further information which you may find useful:

Berne E (1968) *Games People Play; The Psychology of Human Relationships.* Harmondsworth: Penguin.

Argyle M (1983) *The Psychology of Interpersonal Behaviour,* 4th edn. Harmondsworth: Penguin

Beck R C (1986) *Applying Psychology: Understanding People,* 2nd edn. London: Prentice-Hall.

Why Do We Communicate?

Having examined what communication is, it is logical to ask the question 'Why do we communicate?' The answer may seem apparent – after all communicating is commonplace, isn't it?

 Before progressing further consider why you communicate. Make notes as these will prove useful later.

Below are some typical responses that are given to the question: 'Why do we communicate?'

'It's natural . . .'

'To gain knowledge/information . . .'

'It is self-serving . . .'

'For social interactions . . .'

'Necessary for survival . . .'

'Lets our needs be known . . .'

'Breaks down barriers . . .'

'Lets us function as people . . .'

These reasons explaining why we communicate represent a cross-section of people's ideas; none of them is necessarily wrong but the answer is rather more complex than identifying isolated characteristics.

Communication is something many people take for granted, and perhaps in addressing the question above you may have felt that the responses were somewhat obvious; but on reflection are they? The ability to communicate is a prime requirement for our effectiveness as carers, yet communicating well is problematic. People without doubt respond differently to the same message and seek different outcomes from communication. We turn to the fields of psychology and philosophy for some explanations.

Argyle as stated earlier, argues that through a process of social interactions with others, we can attempt to achieve our individual goals and needs. A primary means by which we 'collaborate' is communication; we communicate in order to achieve, and to make our needs known to others.

Sartre's profound observation may have numerous interpretations, but he is undoubtedly implying that we need relationships and interactions with others, and that through these interactions we can establish a personal identity, form the identities of those with whom we have a relationship and apply meaning to our experiences.

At the fundamental level, humans communicate to survive, to live. On a more sophisticated level, humans use communication to function as an integrated unit in society, as people. To survive and to function in society to the best of our abilities we need to sustain good health and well-being. Communication systems ensure the fulfilment of four different, yet integral, needs which maintain a healthy life-style.

Below are discussed the 'four needs of communication'. Following the description of each need there is a question for you to answer. Where applicable, references for further reading are suggested. Note down your responses to each question. Discussion with colleagues would be appropriate for this activity.

It is intended that you will be able to relate these needs to caring for a patient/client, and also to question your own influences on the communication process. It would also be beneficial to relate each issue to your chosen branch/field of care.

Physical Needs

Without a means of communication we could not acknowledge the state of our physical health. Communication enables human beings to express the physical symptoms of ill health, while enabling them to maintain fitness and well-being. We can collaborate with others to maintain health or to regain it. Indeed, medical research suggests that the absence of interpersonal relationships can in fact jeopardise health.

See Totman R (1987) *Social Causes of Illness*, 2nd edn, pp. 124–130. London: Souvenir Press (Educational and Academic).

Think about how being ill affects a person's ability to communicate physical needs. What do you think might be the consequences of the effect? Also consider how people with disabling conditions such as hearing impairment, speech impairment and sight impairment or who use alternative communication systems to speech are affected by the potential inability to express their physical needs.

Identity Needs

The process of communication enables us to develop our identity. Personal interaction with others enables us to see ourselves as others see us. From these interactions we learn whether we are seen as 'good' or 'bad'; 'attractive' or 'unattractive', 'happy' or 'sad'. It is difficult to make these decisions alone; other people are needed to reinforce these characteristics. You acquire an identity through communicating with others as they in turn acquire an identity from you.

See Argyle M (1983) *The Psychology of Interpersonal Behaviour*, 4th edn, pp. 187–206. Harmondsworth: Penguin.

Adler R B and Towne N (1990) *Looking out; Looking in*, 6th edn, p. 9. Fort Worth: Holt Rinehart and Winston.

As nurses and midwives you will take on the identity of a carer, while those in your care will be identified as patients/clients. These identities carry certain characteristics or roles with them – one of which is the 'sick role' of the patient. What might be the effect of reinforcing the 'sick role' of a client/patient?

How may the process of communication between the nurse and the client/patient be influenced once these identities are established?

Social Needs

Social needs can be considered to comprise three components:

1 *Inclusion* – the need to feel a sense of *belonging*.

2 *Control* – a desire to *influence* others and feel power over one's life.

3 *Affection* – or *respect*. The regard that others have for you is important to your perceptions of social standing, and position in society.

See Argyle M (1983) *The Psychology of Interpersonal Behaviour,* 4th edn, pp. 263–283. Harmondsworth: Penguin.

Adler R B and Towne N (1990) *Looking Out, Looking In: Interpersonal Communication*, 6th edn, pp. 9–10. Fort Worth: Holt Rinehart and Winston.

How might these three components be affected by a disabling condition, ill-health or restricted life opportunities, for example?

Practical Needs

Practical needs are concerned with those everyday functions that require communication. Practical needs such as purchasing food, buying clothes, getting much needed repairs done, are achieved only through some means of communication. Giving information, doing well during interviews, seeking advice from tutors, are all practical needs. Meeting practical needs in turn facilitates achievement of major goals.

See Maslow A H (1968) *The Psychology of Being.* New York: Van Nostrand and Reinhold. This examines the sphere of human need in some detail.

When a person becomes ill or reliant on another, these 'practical needs' are often achieved through the carer. What might be the short- and long-term effects of this relationship on the individual concerned?

Physical Needs

During illness, some people find it difficult to say what is wrong with them. Also when one is ill it can be difficult to maintain those activities that maintain fitness and health – eating, sleeping, exercise; even going out can be a problem. Being unwell is an antisocial pastime. How often have you been ill and discovered that your friends and family do not want to come into contact with your ailment?

For people who have auditory, speech or visual impairments or who use other means of communication, having an illness may serve to reinforce personally felt inadequacies and exacerbate isolation within the social setting.

Identity Needs

Reinforcement of the 'sick' role denies the patient/client personal identity because the process focuses on the illness, disorder or disability rather than the person. If this happens, the communications between the patient/client and carer may become restricted and orientated towards the 'curative' role and the 'sickness' of the person concerned (as discussed in Chapter 3). When these roles become foremost in the relationship, there is a possibility that the patient/client will become dependent upon the carer and thus suffer loss of autonomy.

Social Needs

As pointed out when discussing physical needs, illness can cause isolation. With isolation may be associated a loss of the sense of belonging. In Chapter 3 it was noted that prejudices against illness, disability or disorder can increase social isolation. The concept of self-control is paramount to autonomy. When a person is reliant upon another, when hospitalised, control is often surrendered to the carer. Loss of control hinders self-respect, especially so if the nurse/midwife insists on a strict maintenance of the distinction between the 'sick' person and the 'professional' carer. That is, the carer maintains social distancing.

Practical Needs

When practical needs are affected the results can include the following:

- feelings of inadequacy
- a sense of isolation and loss
- growing dependency on others
- feeling of being a burden on family/friends
- social incompetence . . .

It becomes apparent that through communication human beings are capable of expressing their holistic needs. If methods of communication are mutually compatible, the carer can receive signals which provide information about the individual's ability to express their needs.

Nurses, midwives, social workers, and others in the caring sector must be able to understand people's needs in order to assist them in either regaining or developing the ability to care for themselves. Recognising and understanding the signs that indicate when a person requires assistance enable the process of caring to begin. This process may involve numerous people, including professionals – families, volunteers and of course the patients/clients themselves. Communication between many people, as in multidisciplinary teams which consist of people with different backgrounds, with differing social, cultural and subcultural beliefs and experiences, and often with differing professional perspectives, can present problems which influence the effectiveness of the caring process. A variety of interpretations of patient/client need may arise; what has become central to the client/carer relationship is the primary emphasis on *asking the patient/client* what his or her needs are. The next part of the text moves on to examine how dependency on assistance may hinder the achievement of true potential.

Often the carer can, inadvertently, through misunderstanding, enthusiasm, or ignorance, take over a person's life. This may seem to be in the best interests of the person concerned and occasionally this may be true. But often such action takes away the very potential and independence the patient/client strives to achieve.

The achievement of potential is crucially associated with:

1 *Decision making*

2 *The self-concept*

3 *Autonomy*

When people's ability to communicate effectively becomes dependent upon another person – an interpreter – they can begin to lose not only their identity, but also the capability to direct their own affairs.

This activity has two parts, the first relating to well-being, the second to ill-health.

You, Others and Well-being

Think about and reflect upon the significant people in your life (e.g. wife/husband, children, tutor, bank manager). Make a list of the five people who are most significant.

Now consider the interactions and communications that take place between these people and yourself. How does the relationship you have with these people influence and affect your life in terms of:

● Making decisions?

● Your concept of self?

- Your ability to direct your own affairs (autonomy)?

You, Others and Ill-health
Now think about how your interactions and communications with your five significant people would be affected if you were suddenly faced with being ill, disabled or disadvantaged in some way. It would be beneficial if you could relate this part of the activity to your chosen field of care (see possibilities below). How might your interactions change? How might communications differ? Would the nature of the relationship alter?

We appreciate that for many readers this may be difficult to imagine (unless you are at present ill, disabled or disadvantaged) but establishing understanding of, and identification with, the ill, disabled or disadvantaged patient/client at this stage will greatly enhance your ability to meet his or her needs in the future.

Possibilities

1 You have recently suffered a cerebral vascular accident . . .

2 You have suddenly been made homeless . . .

3 You have developed obsessive behaviour . . .

4 You have become incontinent . . .

5 You are presenting with profoundly challenging behaviour . . .

Without the five significant people identified you might not be able to make decisions, nor develop your self-concept, and though you may be able to direct your own affairs without these people, primarily through relationships with significant others, you would not live the life you are currently experiencing. Assuming that you are in good health you probably feel that you are reasonably in control of your life?

What helps you to believe that you have control over your life is the fact that it is you that articulates with significant people, it is you that can advocate for yourself should the need arise and it is you that promotes your interests. The degree to which people are able, and willing, to perform the activities above is dependent upon their self-concept, as this partly determines the way in which communication is used, and also affects how others respond to their communication.

See Adler R B and Towne N (1990) *Looking Out, Looking In: Interpersonal Communication*, 6th ed., pp. 55–72. Fort Worth: Holt Rinehart and Winston for a clear exposition of this idea.

For this activity the authors considered two significant persons:

Partner – the partner provides the relationship with many qualities including:

> *Encouragement*
>
> *Companionship*
>
> *Belonging and status*

The partner reinforces the ability to make decisions, and is also involved in many of these decisions. They also influence decisions through identifying some of the consequences that may occur. Through the process of interpersonal interaction, the author (and partner) develop an increased self-awareness. While the author has the ability and capability to make decisions alone, there is the need to consider another person, a person who has a great influence upon decisions made.

Immediate Line Manager – here the relationship involves a different set of qualities:

> *Direction*
>
> *Leadership*
>
> *Belonging and worth*
>
> *Authority*
>
> *Understanding*

The relationship with the line manager is one of inequality because of the vertical hierarchy within the organisation. The interactions that take place are frequently related to policy and practice and are more formal than those with the author's partner. Managers will often provide direction and guidance as part of the responsibilities of their role. In this situation the author's autonomy at work may be constrained and with it the opportunity for control over work activities.

Responses to disablement, illness or disadvantage will be different, but experience suggests that you have stated that you would still interact with significant others. But would interactions be the same? How much control would you imagine you might have over the decisions you are capable of making? Would your self-concept alter? Would you retain your autonomy? Whatever your answers it is likely that your interactions with others will carry different levels of influence from those previously experienced.

Irrespective of whether you are caring for a person who has arguably always been disadvantaged in our society, e.g. a person with learning disability, or for one who has recently become so as a result of illness or disablement, it is imperative that interactions with the person do not reinforce lack of influence or inability to express needs. Denial of the patients/clients and their potential may also deny them a rightful place in society. In this respect the nurse or midwife acts as a role model for other members of society, showing acceptance of, and empathy with, the patient or client.

A positive self-concept facilitates personal communications with, and confidence in, others. The nurse or midwife is a figure of authority for patients/clients and as such is a tremendous influence on their self-concept. Just how much an influence can be illustrated by Figure 5.4.

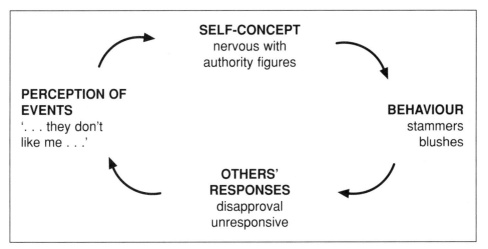

Figure 5.4.   The negative effects of poor self-concept on communication

It is sometimes difficult to comprehend how carers might reinforce a negative self-concept; such action seems to contradict the caring principle. Below are quotations from carers regarding their feelings towards some of the people they have cared for:

'It is easier (communicating) when their eyes are open . . .'

'It's like talking to that wall over there . . .'

Both these remarks were made by carers who, at the time, cared for people in intensive care units.

See Ashworth P M (1980) *Care to Communicate: an investigation into problems of communication between patients and nurses in intensive therapy units,* p. 82. London: Royal College of Nursing.

How hard do you think it might have been for these carers to hide their true feelings? In such situations it is difficult to maintain effective communication, to feel that one is being effective in practice. It becomes difficult to maintain positive interactions. But maintained they must be; the carer should avoid seeking the solace of non-comprehension, believing that lack of response signals lack of understanding or feeling. Developing the confidence and capability to communicate with *all* patients/clients, irrespective of their social or health difficulties, is a key objective for the effective practitioner.

Figure 5.5 illustrates the positive effects of the patient/client having a secure self-concept. The more autonomous patients/clients are, and the greater their role in making decisions for themselves, the more effective you have been as a communicator and practitioner.

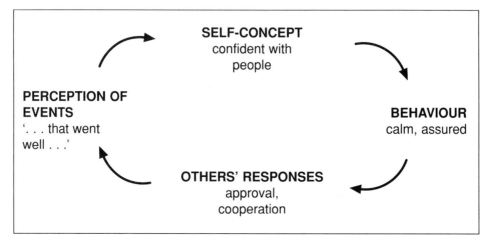

Figure 5.5. The positive effects of developing good self-concept

Non-verbal and Verbal Communication

The effects of both non-verbal (NVC) and verbal communication (VC) upon the care that you provide for a person should not be underestimated. The topics themselves are so vast, and at times so personal to ourselves and the situations we find ourselves in, that they cannot be fully addressed in this chapter. Reading materials will be suggested, however, which can provide you with an extensive insight into these complex and fascinating aspects of communication.

This section has been particularly designed to introduce the reader to NVC as applied to caring. Without non-verbal and verbal communication skills our lives would be indescribably different.

Non-verbal Communication

Non-verbal communication is a means of communication transmitted through a complex, and often involuntary, use of signals and symbols. As you discovered earlier, communication is sent through channels to a receiver, the message needing to be encoded and decoded. This same principle applies to NVC. Frequently, and not uncommonly within the caring sector, the sender is unaware of the signals he or she is transmitting and this can often result in the receiver being hurt or confused because the NVC and VC do not complement one another. Non-verbal communication can be divided into two parts:

1 **Body Language** – the signals are transmitted by the body and the channels for such communication include:

   Posture

   Gesture

   Body contact/touch

   Eye contact

   Spatial proximity

   The mime artist makes extraordinarily good use of body language.

2 **Symbolic Representation** – communication facilitated through the use of single or interconnected symbols, e.g.

   Written word

   Sounds

   Visual images

   Clothing

   Appearance

   Social sight vocabulary

   Dramatists, cartoonists, writers, fashion designers and musicians make excellent use of symbolic representation.

NVC is applicable to all people irrespective of race, culture or country of origin, but people from different backgrounds and cultures to your own may interpret your signals in ways that would be detrimental to the relationship. For instance, people in France, of both sexes, may greet each other by kissing on the cheeks, while in the United Kingdom people tend to shake hands. If you were unaware of these differences imagine how you would feel if on your first visit to France someone of the same sex attempted to kiss you: the results could be highly entertaining or, more likely, highly embarrassing. Awareness of cultural, racial, ethnic and spiritual differences can prevent embarrassment and misunderstanding between both parties. This process of awareness and its centrality to effective caring is a theme of this book and in particular Chapter 3.

Some examples of NVC were given earlier. Now these will be examined in more detail.

Body Language

Posture
The posture of a person often indicates his or her current attitude or emotional state. Practising the use of body language with friends, colleagues or fellow

students can enhance the effectiveness of formal communications with clients/patients at a later date. Try communicating a message using only body language. See if you can maintain a conversation without speaking.

Some postures are reasonably straightforward to decode, but others can be more complex. Irrespective of the complexity of the posture you adopt, however, do not underestimate the power of the messages you convey to the patient/client. Consider the effect on a client/patient who has just asked 'Is it serious, nurse?' and whom is responded to by the nurse with shrugged shoulders.

Unfortunately, some patients/clients may not have total control over their posture. This can be due to a variety of factors.

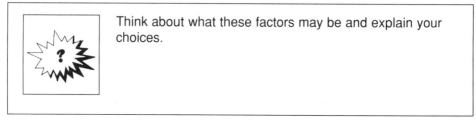

Think about what these factors may be and explain your choices.

The degree of physical ability of the person is important as is his or her mental well-being and physical health. Severe depression may reduce the individual to such a regressed state that the posture becomes one resembling that of the unborn fetus. Age also plays its part; young children have yet to master full bodily control and increasing age may alter postural flexibility.

Certain situations and events may lead us to lose control over our bodies, even if for only a short period of time. Some of these precipitants may be imposed on patients/clients by their illness/condition or by the prescribed treatment. Treatments, while instigated in the best interests of the patient/client, can often have temporary, or permanent, effects on postural control. Examples might include:

- Drugs

- Electro-convulsive therapy (ECT)

- Anaesthesia

- Surgery

Common conditions influencing posture include cerebral palsy, motor neurone disease and muscular dystrophy.

Posture communicates a tremendous amount of information – endeavour to make your posture appropriate to the moment. The posture required for a counselling session will be markedly different to that used during a formal interview.

Gesture

Frequently, speech and thought are accompanied by gestures. Gestures, in terms of body language, differ from the gestures used in symbolic representation because their application is considerably more extensive.

Kendon (1972) suggests that gestures form an integral part of 'total communication'. He also states that they have four functions.

Reflect upon what these functions may be. When you have compiled your list compare it with Kendon's given below.

Kendon's four functions of gesture are:

1 To display the structure of an utterance by enumerating elements or showing how they are grouped.

2 To point at people and/or objects.

3 To provide emphasis.

4 To illustrate shape, size, or movements, particularly if these are difficult to explain in words.

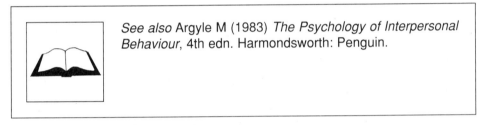

See also Argyle M (1983) *The Psychology of Interpersonal Behaviour*, 4th edn. Harmondsworth: Penguin.

To assess the credibility of Kendon's suggestions attempt to talk to a friend on a subject you know well, but one into which your friend has little insight, and make this attempt without the use of gestures. The 'alternative' communication methods mentioned below utilise Kendon's functional analysis of gestures, which may partly explain why these languages can be learned by those of us who would generally communicate through speech and/or the written word. By utilising gestures effectively carers can readily communicate with the majority of sighted clients/patients as well as those with specialised communication needs. For example, the carer can communicate with hearing-impaired individuals, or those with speech defects, through formalised systems of gestures such as the Makaton Sign Language, British Sign Language or the Derbyshire Language Scheme.

Suggested further reading:

Morris D (1979) *Gestures, Their Origins and Distribution.* London: Cape.

Pease A (1984) *Body Language – How to Read Others' Thoughts by their Gestures.* London: Sheldon Press.

The use of sign language has its roots in the cultural context. For instance, American Sign Language differs from its British counterpart despite them both being based on the English language.

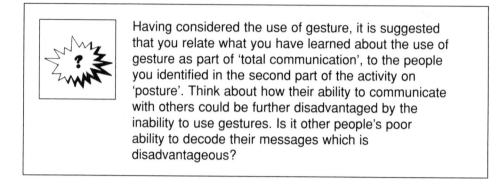

Having considered the use of gesture, it is suggested that you relate what you have learned about the use of gesture as part of 'total communication', to the people you identified in the second part of the activity on 'posture'. Think about how their ability to communicate with others could be further disadvantaged by the inability to use gestures. Is it other people's poor ability to decode their messages which is disadvantageous?

Body Contact

Argyle (1983) says that body contact is the most primitive form of social behaviour and is a powerful communicator. There are numerous cultural influences on the use of touch, some of which have already been discussed. Touch is a sensory mechanism, being one of the five special senses (touch, taste, sight, hearing and smell). Thus not only can we receive messages about the nature of our environment at any given time but we are also able to communicate with others by the appropriate application of touch.

People touch others for a variety of different reasons, and the relationships these people have with each other will affect the way they touch. With this in mind think about how, and what, you communicate through touch to the following list of people:

- Brother or sister
- Mother or father
- Husband or wife
- Friend (female or male)
- Lover

Jourard (1966) discussed the touching of a person's body as an indication of intimacy and the relationship between the people concerned. Figure 5.6 is a diagrammatic representation of Jourard's research indicating who is touched by whom, and on which parts of their anatomy.

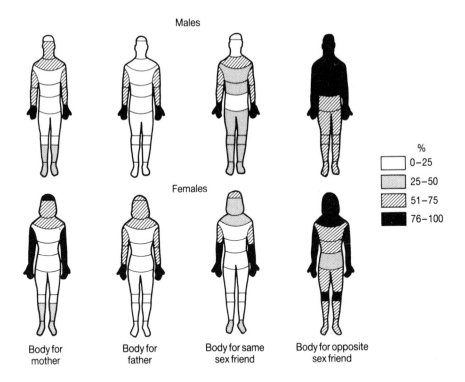

Males

Females

%
0–25
25–50
51–75
76–100

| Body for mother | Body for father | Body for same sex friend | Body for opposite sex friend |

Figure 5.6. Jourard – male and female experience of touch from others. Reproduced with kind permission from Argyle M, (1983) *The Psychology of Interpersonal Behaviour*, 4th Edition. Harmondsworth: Penguin.

You may have noted from your own responses that touching becomes more intimate as development away from your family increases and you form relationships which are external to the family; therefore it is logical to assume that *what* you are communicating also becomes more intimate. For instance, sexual interest is noted by an increase in touching behaviours and by the area of touch being extended to include areas of the body not usually touched during ordinary social exchanges. It is through these various levels of touching that the participants communicate a variety of emotional feelings, and this process also communicates to onlookers information regarding the relationship (Morris, 1977).

Complementary therapies such as massage, Shiatsu and aromatherapy make extensive use of touch to engender physical and emotional health. In this way the practical application of touch becomes as therapeutic as its effective use as a tool of communication.

Nurses and midwives, along with other health care professionals, have been accorded by their role the right to touch people who might be complete strangers in the most intimate manner. Adult nursing provides examples of this with the procedures that are necessary to insert a catheter and suppository (French, 1989). The degree of intimacy poses several moral and ethical questions.

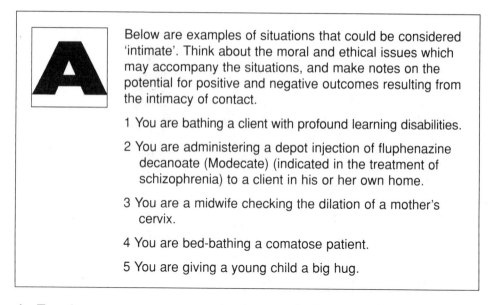

Below are examples of situations that could be considered 'intimate'. Think about the moral and ethical issues which may accompany the situations, and make notes on the potential for positive and negative outcomes resulting from the intimacy of contact.

1 You are bathing a client with profound learning disabilities.

2 You are administering a depot injection of fluphenazine decanoate (Modecate) (indicated in the treatment of schizophrenia) to a client in his or her own home.

3 You are a midwife checking the dilation of a mother's cervix.

4 You are bed-bathing a comatose patient.

5 You are giving a young child a big hug.

As French states, carers are permitted to touch those cared for in the most intimate of ways, but unlike the relationships discussed in the last activity the formal caring relationship is not one that has normally developed through a selection process. You will possibly have noted that many more questions arise, perhaps, than are answered.

Situation 1

Normally the length of time that you have known an individual affects the degree of intimacy, but frequently you will be bathing virtual strangers who place themselves into your trust. You may be washing someone's genital area, an action not normally associated with a relationship between two strangers, and even if you are not physically implementing care you may be supervising the client – how many of us would respond favourably to a complete stranger observing us in the bath? The ethical considerations are wide-ranging and would include consideration of exploitation/abuse (of position/power/trust) and human rights (privacy/dignity/association/choice).

The gender of the nurse is also an issue, as it relates to the gender of the client. Do male clients feel more secure with female nurses; would they prefer a male nurse? The high proportion of women in nursing may effectively afford little choice in this area.

Situation 2

In this situation the dilemmas may not appear so obvious as those highlighted above because the action of administering an injection is associated closely with treatment and therefore gives the action respectable purpose. But when you consider the action, you begin to realise the intimacy involved. The administration of an injection involves the recipient undressing in some way and in addition the procedure is carried out in privacy – there is no external onlooker. The issues of exploitation, abuse and infringement of a person's human rights apply. Physical assault is clearly related to consent for the procedure and whether this is obtained or not.

Situation 3

Although this is predominantly an action carried out by one female with another there still exists the 'stranger' factor above. The midwife is touching probably the most personal part of another human being's body and the woman's levels of embarrassment and discomfort are likely to be high. The issue is further complicated by the exercise of choice. Women have available a range of childbirth techniques which involve differing applications, and degrees, of touch. This choice means that the midwife must be flexible but also provides the means for the woman to sanction a particular approach and thus the intimacy of touch that may accompany it.

Further complexity is introduced when the examination is carried out by a male doctor or medical student. Does the title 'doctor' serve as justification for the intimacy of touch? Do all women perceive this to be the case?

Situation 4

There are many parallels in this example with those discussed above – except that the patient is unable to express his or her objections to your actions and hence can be very vulnerable to abuse. Dignity and privacy remain important to the unconscious patient and the onus is clearly on the nurse to promote and maintain these elements.

Situation 5

This is surely the most innocent of actions and one which the majority of people will have experienced during their own childhood. But how might this sign of affection be interpreted by the child's parents? The carer is performing a role that the parents may be either inexperienced in or incapable of performing for themselves at that moment. This can lead to feelings of jealousy and inadequacy within the parents. Additionally, the intimacy of your touch can be misinterpreted by the child and this too can prove difficult, particularly when it comes to terminating the relationship you have developed.

If you are working with children who have faced the trauma of physical and sexual abuse, you will need to be particularly aware of the messages your touch communicates to the children concerned.

Suggested reading includes:

Finkelhor D (1988) *Nursery Crimes – Sexual Abuse in Daycare.* Newbury Park: Sage Publications.

Morris D (1977) *Manwatching: A Field Guide to Human Behaviour.* London: Cape.

There are, as identified, many situations where touching a patient/client will possibly result in either yourselves or others questioning the moral and/or ethical considerations of your actions. As carers you cannot deny patients/clients the benefits of touch, for touch is a human need. Because society has put its faith in you by allowing carers, as French so aptly puts it, 'the permission to touch', you are also held responsible and accountable for your actions. The five examples examined are common situations which arise daily within the delivery of care, and fortunately for the vast majority of carers their actions are never brought into question. This is due to many factors including effective leadership, positive role-models, knowledge of procedures and policies, effective skills and personal integrity. Abusing the carer's privileged use of touch will result in societal disapproval, possibly legal consequences, and professional sanctions as administered by the UKCC.

Eye Contact

The eyes not only give messages to others but also in turn facilitate the interpretation of the attitudes, feelings and attentions of those others. The use of gaze has also been shown to synchronise speech (Argyle, 1983).

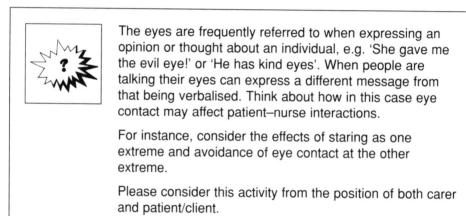

The eyes are frequently referred to when expressing an opinion or thought about an individual, e.g. 'She gave me the evil eye!' or 'He has kind eyes'. When people are talking their eyes can express a different message from that being verbalised. Think about how in this case eye contact may affect patient–nurse interactions.

For instance, consider the effects of staring as one extreme and avoidance of eye contact at the other extreme.

Please consider this activity from the position of both carer and patient/client.

The degree of contact people make with their eyes is dependent on several factors such as:

- The situation, e.g. formal or informal
- The status of the parties involved
- The topic of conversation
- The relationship between the people interacting, e.g. friend or family

The avoidance of eye contact can indicate shyness, insecurity or inattentiveness; conversely, strong eye contact may indicate confidence, assurance or concentration. Eye contact can also signal the stages of a conversation, which is useful information when counselling people (see Argyle, 1983). When you are interacting with a patient/client always be aware of the strength of your eye contact. Staring can be intimidating and weak eye contact can result in your patient/client feeling unsure of your convictions. As the relationship between you and your patient/client develops so too will the understanding of the signals sent out by both parties.

It is very difficult, if not impossible, for us to lie with our eyes. Hess (1975) believes that the eyes may give the most revealing and accurate of all communication signals. This is because they provide people with a focus point on the body, an invisible contact between ourselves and the person with whom we interact. The importance of this in preserving meaningful relationships must not be overlooked by the carer. You may find it beneficial to 'practise' eye contact with your colleagues and with people in authority (e.g. your tutors or mentors), as these people will provide you with opportunities to discover where eye contact reveals much about their, and your, inner thoughts.

Spatial Proximity

The term 'personal space' is an often-used expression describing an invisible barrier that is created by people around themselves and within which they feel comfortable. Acceptance of physical proximity has cultural and racial variants. One fact about spatial proximity is consistent in all cultures, though, and that is that one's personal space can all too easily be invaded.

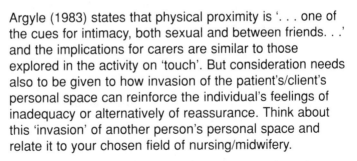

Argyle (1983) states that physical proximity is '. . . one of the cues for intimacy, both sexual and between friends. . .' and the implications for carers are similar to those explored in the activity on 'touch'. But consideration needs also to be given to how invasion of the patient's/client's personal space can reinforce the individual's feelings of inadequacy or alternatively of reassurance. Think about this 'invasion' of another person's personal space and relate it to your chosen field of nursing/midwifery.

What might be the result of a carer's intervention when a patient/client is struggling to dress him or herself?

If a patient/client is discovered by you to be crying, what could result from you entering their personal space?

Each individual has a different 'personal space' and the caring process should respect this. The implications of invading someone's space are allied to those discussed in 'touch' (see Hall, 1959) and it is all too easy to offend people by 'getting too close' or by 'remaining too distant'. Being too close can make people feel uncomfortable and ill at ease, while being distant can signal to people an air of aloofness and a 'cool relationship'. When considering the caring relationship, both of these extremes might result in the client/patient feeling aggressive (too close) or neglected (too distant).

For the two examples given above there is no definite answer, but when you intervene to dress someone the person may resent your interference, or may allow you to take over, neither situation necessarily being desirable. However, all situations require assessment according to their merits and situations will exist where the individual is in need of your intervention. If the person resents your interference then the relationship will be damaged, especially if action has highlighted an inadequacy. In the first example, the patient/client may become dependent upon you to fulfil his or her basic needs, a situation that is not conducive to the patient's/client's development and well-being.

In example 2, intervention could be seen as an intrusion into what is already a very personal situation and may result in resentment. Conversely, you may provide the individual with an appropriate shoulder to cry on. French gives a very clear example of the effects a carer's proximity can have on the individual:

> *When someone approaches another individual, for instance*
> *when a nurse walks towards a patient, a great deal of*
> *anticipation is experienced by that person ('What is she going to*
> *do to me?').*

FRENCH, 1989

As carers you are invariably going to interact with people within a personal relationship, be it as named nurses, key workers or otherwise. In order to make those interactions, and subsequent relationships, positive ones, respect for the individual's personal space is important.

Suggested further reading:

Adler R B and Towne N (1990) *Looking Out, Looking In – Interpersonal Communication,* 6th edn. Fort Worth: Holt, Rinehart and Winston.

Hall E T (1959) *The Silent Language.* New York: Doubleday.

An individual's 'personal space' is difficult to ascertain until a relationship has developed with that individual. Even when the relationship has formed, it remains possible to invade the individual's space during interactions. Carers must be alert to what is, in effect, this intrusion into someone's privacy. The close proximity between patient/client and nurse required by the caring process, while it helps effective care interventions, may result in discomfiture or embarrassment for both parties. Awareness of spatial proximity and its potential effects is therefore important when you are seeking to communicate effectively as a practitioner.

Facial Expression
Allied to eye contact, but also an important component in its own right, facial

expression conveys many signals from the sender, especially signals related to the sender's emotional states.

According to Ekman et al (1972) there are seven main facial expressions depicting emotions. These emotions are well known to all humans, irrespective of race, culture or social background and can be decoded quite readily by us all.

Reflect on what these seven emotions might be and make a note of them.

Ekman's seven identified emotions correlated with facial expression are:

- Happiness
- Surprise
- Fear
- Sadness
- Anger
- Disgust (contempt)
- Interest

These emotions are communicated through the way humans smile, frown or raise eyebrows and by the configuration of the mouth. The latter two are worth further investigation, as eyebrow and mouth signals can communicate a wealth of information (Argyle, 1983). Although these emotions can be reasonably well told apart from one another, it is easy for confusion to occur. For example, fear and anger may be manifest in similar facial expressions. It is also beneficial to note that 'surprise' and 'interest' are not true emotions, but are cognitive reactions.

While these seven emotions are expressed in all cultures, they can, as noted by Shimoda et al (1978), be open to misinterpretation when people from different cultures attempt to interpret facial expressions that are unfamiliar to them. This is an important consideration when caring in a multicultural society. Recognising the influence of facial expressions upon the people you care for, and upon the colleagues that you work with, becomes an important factor in the practitioner role.

Think about a person who has recently discovered he or she has a terminal illness and only weeks to live. You are the friend he or she confides in. Your reactions to this disclosure will be partly expressed on your face and thus will be transmitted to your friend. Focusing on each of Ekman's seven emotional expressions in turn, try to imagine how your friend would feel on seeing your reactions, and speculate on the effect they may have.

Depending upon your personality and the relationship you have with the person concerned, you might initially display any one of the seven emotions, although displaying happiness is probably unlikely. If you were unaware of the severity of the illness your initial reaction might be one of surprise or sadness, fear or anger – surprise because of the unexpected news, sadness because a friend is about to die, fear because this disclosure may remind you of your own mortality, anger resulting from a sense of uselessness and/or loss. You could experience disgust arising from the lack of effective treatment and the failure of the health care provision to assist your friend's recovery. If you were not actually familiar with the person, your first reaction might be one of interest – for instance, interest in the illness or maybe an egocentric speculation as to why this person chose you to confide in.

Though a reaction of happiness is unlikely, could it occur? If you knew this friend very well, and were aware that they had been suffering tremendously because of the illness, and in addition both of you felt that death would be a release from the suffering, perhaps then a reaction of happiness could be possible. Admittedly, happiness is not an emotion associated with death, but human emotions are unpredictable; and on occasions happiness can be found in the most unlikely circumstances.

During the course of the conversation with your friend you may have displayed all of the facial expressions which Ekman describes. Their effects on your friend will depend upon his or her state of mind, trust in you, the intimacy of the relationship, his or her knowledge of the illness and your knowledge of the illness, among other factors. One aspect is certain: that is, that your non-verbal communication may either enable your friend to talk through his or her experiences or conversely make him or her feel guilty or unwanted, or experience any number of negative feelings. Although this activity examines an extreme example, the consequences of inappropriate facial expressions can be difficult to retrieve once set in motion.

It is difficult to pre-empt what a person will tell us in conversation and our reactions can be even more unpredictable. In a profession where effective communication is essential, such variables can be extremely stimulating, hopelessly embarrassing or provide for complexity of interaction. Your interactions, however, will have a profound impact upon the people you care for. This is particularly true if you need to counsel patients/clients when body language can frequently communicate with greater clarity than the spoken word.

Symbolic Representation

Symbolic representation is a mode of communicating that cannot be ignored. This section highlights the most significant aspects of symbolism and their relationship to caring. The activities in this section are designed to increase awareness of symbolism, to illustrate its possible use and to facilitate understanding of its meaning and effect.

Symbols are used throughout our lives to represent the world in which we live and are frequently utilised where, or when, other forms of communication would be either inappropriate or inordinately complex, e.g. road traffic signs. Symbols can also become synonymous with many aspects of life, and may often be described according to their meaning.

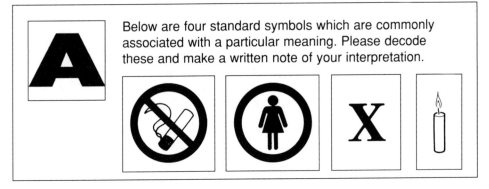

Below are four standard symbols which are commonly associated with a particular meaning. Please decode these and make a written note of your interpretation.

Interpretation of the four symbols very much depends upon life experience, but you will probably have responded to this activity as follows:

The 'No Smoking' Symbol
For many people who smoke cigarettes this symbol represents not only a warning not to smoke but also a restriction of their lifestyle. For non-smokers it may be a guarantee of a smoke-free environment. The standard use of the colour red with such signs is central to the meaning.

The Ladies' Toilet Symbol
You may have interpreted this symbol differently because of its widespread usage. It clearly relates to women, but they could be of indeterminate age. It might thus be applied to any woman-only service or female child service, but in this instance we are using it as the symbol found outside ladies' toilets.

The X Symbol
The 'X' represents the Roman numeral for the number ten. It also represents the multiplication symbol in arithmetic calculations. For many it is symbolic of love for another person, being a visual representation of the act of kissing.

The Candle
The candle may be symbolic of many things. A church, a wedding, or perhaps a funeral. Candles are often strongly associated with peace and hope. It may possibly be considered a symbol of festive occasions such as Christmas. It may represent nursing by evoking memories of Florence Nightingale or be symbolic of a time before the advent of the use of gas and electricity for lighting.

You are able to interpret these symbols using the processes identified previously in the chapter. The symbols transmit a signal, you receive it, decode it and you understand the meaning . . . or do you?

Think about the following situation, and then answer the question that follows.

. . . a couple from Jupiter visit Earth for a vacation, and spend some time in Britain. Wishing to see as much of the country as possible they decide to hire a car at the spaceport and fortunately Earth cars work on the same principle as those at home. Unfortunately the couple from Jupiter ended their vacation at the first road junction when both were killed in a fatal road traffic accident . . .

Why did the couple from Jupiter die?

The tourists from Jupiter were unaware that a 'red triangle' is symbolic of danger in Britain, their experience of symbols being different. Thus the traffic symbol at the road junction was meaningless. But even with experience of symbolic understanding discrimination is still needed if a symbol has many meanings. If British drivers were similarly unable to discriminate they too could experience the tragic accident that befell the people from Jupiter . . . after all what is a red triangle other than three lines joined together and coloured red? If Jupitans do not visualise in colour, or use different colour schemes, explaining to them that red means danger may be difficult. Consider how clients/patients with colour blindness may be affected. Would they be able to make use of such symbolic representation effectively? Would they share the same understanding of a coloured symbol as a person with standard colour perception?

The language of symbols is learned in the same way other forms of communication are learned. That is, through tuition, through experience, through usage and through observation.

Reflect on the patient/client who cannot use speech, is unable to write and does not understand any recognised alternative communication systems.

How might communication be possible?

Responses to this activity are limited only by imagination. Whatever the reason for the inability to communicate via the more common systems, carers can, after assessing the person's capabilities, devise an appropriate communication system that is understandable to all concerned. Such a system could include picture cards to depict various needs or a series of flash cards. Touch and gesture can be used in conjunction with your system, and will extend the system's vocabulary. An important element is the need for consistency in order for patients/clients and carers alike to become familiar with the system. It is advantageous to develop a system that is flexible and adaptive, as this better serves individual need.

French (1989, pp. 66–70) gives three useful examples of alternative systems, originally designed by The Chest, Heart and Stroke Association (Tavistock House, Tavistock Square, London WC1H 6JE). These have their limitations but do provide ideas for the development of a unique system which might meet the special needs of a chosen patient/client.

Touch and gesture were mentioned above and these enhance the transmission of many symbolic messages.

 Think about the messages that can be transmitted through the use of gesture and touch. Make a note of those that may prove helpful to the caring relationship.

There are many helpful messages which can be transmitted via touch and gesture – for instance, politeness, friendship, warmth, understanding and practical assistance. Unfortunately given the right, or perhaps more accurately the wrong, situations, the signals transmitted may also signify dislike, misunderstanding, coolness and other negative attributes. There are a number of contributory factors aiding the interpretation of touch.

- *What part of the body does the touching.*

- *What part of the body is touched.*

- *How long the touch lasts.*

- *The amount of pressure applied.*

- *Whether there is movement after contact is made.*

- *Whether anyone else is present.*

- *The situation in which the touch occurs.*

- *The relationship between the persons involved.*

ADLER AND TOWNE, 1990

These factors can make touch and the associated gestures a complex language in their own right. In addition, the messages transmitted by these means can be ambiguous and are therefore open to a variety of interpretations. Such interpretations can depend upon a variety of elements such as the gender of the people involved, their ethnic background, their marital status or their social background. This variety of interpretations emphasises the necessity of individually assessing patients/clients in order to understand their specific needs and modes of communication. Holistic assessment engenders understanding for both carer and patient/client and restricts the opportunities for misinterpretation.

The symbolic use of touch and gesture can be very powerful and as such should be employed carefully. Possibly the most profitable application of touch and gesture is to reinforce the spoken word.

Social Sight Vocabulary
These are the signs and symbols that are used to convey a variety of everyday messages, for example road traffic signs, advertisements, shop signs and signs/symbols for public amenities. Nurses who specialise in caring for people with learning disabilities will be aware that understanding social sight vocabulary is important for the development of social skills, developing the ability to integrate within one's own society.

Clothing and Appearance
Both of these components form part of social behaviour, and communicate information about the person. Clothing in particular can become symbolic and convey a variety of messages including information about a person's occupation, status, attractiveness, group membership and even the presence of a conformist or non-conformist attitude (Argyle, 1983).

Clothing and appearance can be regularly changed both as fashions alter and as a person's status changes. Thus they are a very flexible means of communicating messages. Within the caring professions clothing can provide powerful symbolic meaning.

 Think about the symbolism that is provided by clothes and appearance within nursing and midwifery. Note how these symbols may be interpreted by the patients/clients in your care.

---

1 The uniforms worn by adult/child nurses and midwives may be seen as symbolic of caring, by patients, or as a symbol of authority and expert knowledge. Other nurses and midwives may see the uniform as a status symbol or indicator of authority within the care team. Caution must be exercised in the symbolic use of uniforms, though, in order to avoid the dangers of social distancing discussed in Chapter 4. Nurses in the mental health and learning disability fields have recognised the symbolic dangers of uniforms and discarded them in order to enhance the relationships they have with their clients.

2 Badges worn by some nurses are another symbol of status, but also of achievement. Badges denoting a trade/ professional union may symbolise the wearer's political affiliation. Badges, of course, serve a useful purpose as discussed in Chapter 3, when the use of labels was

---

THE INDIVIDUAL IN SOCIETY

considered. Current implementation of *The Patient's Charter* (DOH, 1991) includes the identification of a 'named nurse' for each patient. National Charter Standard Number 8 states that there should be: 'A named qualified nurse, midwife or health visitor responsible for each patient'. Badges serve as one means of identifying the 'named nurse' and thus enable care providers to meet this particular charter standard. However, Chapter 3 also discussed the use of labels and the resultant expectations about behaviour. A nurse being 'named' leads the patient to expect certain behaviour from that nurse that may not always be possible. There may be a subsequent conflict between expectation and reality, leading to a difficult relationship between patient and nurse (the danger of over-promising and under-delivering). On the other hand, understanding by patient and nurse of the 'named nurse' function may enhance the relationship between them and subsequently the quality of care provided; this is the intention of *The Patient's Charter*.

3 Nursing/midwifery belts and buckles – a part of the uniform that symbolises status, position within the care team and possibly authority. Belts and buckles may be seen as functional implements only, but this does not explain the use by some nurses and midwives of elaborate, often costly, buckles in preference to plainer versions.

4 The wearing of hats – often justified on the basis of hygiene. However, clearly some hats could never serve this purpose and appear merely decorative. For those that wear them they can be symbols of achievement, or competence (note the use of rings on hats denoting the experience of nurses in training), or may reflect a pride in the hospital or the profession.

These are some examples of the easily identifiable symbolic uses of clothing and appearance. However, other signals can as easily be projected to the patient/client and their relatives:

e.g. Dirty/crumpled clothes = poor self-image, lack of pride, personal problems, poor self-hygiene, lack of concern for the patient/client?

Imagine how you might react if cared for by someone who, on first sight, appeared dirty, unkempt and generally untidy. Would you have confidence in such an individual? Clearly, image is important, and clothing and appearance have a considerable impact on the perceptions of others.

Clothing and appearance can be a barrier to effective communication, and inhibit effective relationships, but there are also instances when the symbolic meaning of clothing and appearance can provide comfort, reassurance and confidence to the patient/client.

In order to care for people you must be able to understand their needs, including the needs of people whose first 'language' is not the spoken or written word with which the majority of the population is familiar. The alternative languages you may encounter include *Makaton, Blissymbolics, British Sign Language* and *Braille*. The former two examples are often employed with people with learning disabilities when 'standard' communication systems are inappropriate. The latter two, familiar to many of the population, are utilised primarily by people with speech or visual impairment. All these systems have one thing in common – they can be learned, and they are learned in the same way that the written and spoken word are mastered. Inevitably, the nurse or midwife will one day care for a person who communicates using a symbolic or sign language. Being able to communicate with that person in his or her own language will ensure that the care received will be meaningful. If a person is received into care and cannot be communicated with imagine how they will feel – lonely? isolated? ignored? misunderstood? The onus is on the carer to transmit messages in such a way that they can be decoded by the patient/client, a task made considerably less strenuous if communication is in a common language. Below is an activity which is based on your perceptions of the less obvious symbols of status and power.

 Think about the practice areas that you have worked in and consider the situations and interactions you have observed. Make a note of the subtle symbolism found in such situations and interactions. Give thought to such aspects as 'handovers', 'office status', 'meetings' and so on.

It is possible that some readers may have had difficulty in identifying the more subtle examples of symbolism which exist in many care establishments. Nevertheless, they are there if closely observed. For instance, watch where people sit at meetings, observe the movements and interactions that take place within the unit/ward offices. Note also your own position and the symbols of your status as students (*see* Argyle, 1983). Symbols build up an expectation in the patient/client and this is reinforced by carers who live out the expectation. Society also reinforces expectations through media symbolism. Such media symbolism can support the nursing role by emphasising the possession of knowledge and skills which engender trust, confidence and high quality care. Negative symbolism, such as the 'naughty nurse' or 'handmaiden', hinder nursing and midwifery effectiveness. The use of symbolism by the professions can either support or negate societal symbolism. Symbols can enable the patient/client to understand the nurses'/midwives' role, and that of the professions, if these are appropriately applied. Symbols become meaningful if used in this way.

The Written Word

This is possibly the most vital and fundamental of the symbolic languages, and one which many people take for granted. Words are no more than symbols which represent elements of our world – objects, ideas, thoughts, opinions, events and so on. Words are even representative of elements whose very existence we may choose to question – for instance, unicorns, gods, fairies, the devil, ghosts and Robin Hood. Words themselves are composed of lesser symbols called letters. The alphabet and numerals are the component symbols of our language without which the writing, and reading, of this book would be impossible (*see* Adler and Towne, 1990, p. 156).

Within the caring professions, the written word plays a major role in communicating information regarding the patient/client. Writing can be permanent (depending on its mode of storage), whereas the spoken word cannot. Thus writing provides a record of the patient/client that would be lost if we were reliant on the spoken word.

Care plans, individual programme plans (IPP), case notes, fluid balance charts, pathology forms and medical histories, for example, all provide written information to practitioners which enables them best to meet the needs of the individual. In addition, such records allow practitioners to monitor progress, not only with regard to the patient/client but also relating to organisational performance. However, as with all communication systems, there are rules which must be applied effectively in order both to use and to understand the symbolic meaning of written text. By themselves, letters have no real significance; they have to be organised into meaningful arrangements such as words, sentences, phrases and paragraphs.

 Below is an arrangement of letters. Rearrange them into a well-known phrase.
'Te bo ro tno te bo, ttha is eht stqnouei . . .'

The rearranged phrase, as you probably realised, is

'To be or not to be, that is the question . . .'

WILLIAM SHAKESPEARE

Whether you managed to rearrange these letters does not matter; the important point is that no one will have read the sentence immediately. This is because the rules which ensure understanding of the English language are not apparent. What is missing are the syntactic and semantic rules which govern our language. Syntax relates to the way symbols are grammatically structured and arranged. Semantics governs meaning in language and thus, together with syntax, partly determines how you respond to presented text/symbols. The following activity focuses on the appropriate use of written communication.

Think about the following scenario, and imagine that you have actually observed it. After the incident you write about it in the relevant care plan/IPP. Make a note of what you would write.

. . . John is standing before you, leaning across a table; his arm sweeps across the table top, knocking over cups and saucers . . .

Read through what you have written about this scenario, and answer the following:

- Can you understand it?

- Could anyone else understand it?

- Is it accurate?

Possibly you answered 'yes' to all three questions. You may have simply reproduced the text from the activity, which would give it accuracy. However, does simple reproduction enhance understanding? You may have tried to interpret John's actions – to give them meaning. Understanding is inextricably linked with meaning but difficulties arise when interpretations of meaning differ.

To illustrate this further, listed below are some of the possible interpretations of John's behaviour:

1 John is showing aggression

2 John has fainted

3 John is having an epileptic seizure

4 John does not like the tea

5 John would like some attention

6 John needs someone to listen to him

7 John is in pain

8 John is subject to a hallucinatory experience

9 John has had an involuntary muscle spasm

10 John was reaching out for another object on the table

Each of these interpretations makes an assumption about John's behaviour, because the scene witnessed does not provide enough evidence to support such interpretations. The danger of such interpretations is the potential for labelling through the use of such terms as 'aggressive' or 'epileptic'. These issues, you will remember, were explored in greater depth in Chapter 3. Yet we seek to understand human behaviour beyond mere observation and objective recording. Objective recording of what was *actually* observed, as opposed to assumed meaning, gives the practitioner a base-line for further analysis. Careful recording of the 'what' facilitates understanding of the 'why'.

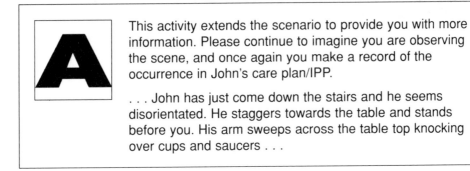

This activity extends the scenario to provide you with more information. Please continue to imagine you are observing the scene, and once again you make a record of the occurrence in John's care plan/IPP.

. . . John has just come down the stairs and he seems disorientated. He staggers towards the table and stands before you. His arm sweeps across the table top knocking over cups and saucers . . .

Your notes now contain more information, and analysis may seem a little easier. Unfortunately there are still ambiguities – for what reason might John be 'disorientated' and 'staggering'? Perhaps he is intoxicated? Maybe he is a diabetic? Is this a reaction to new drugs? Could it be a toxic confusional state? The activity could go on, adding a little more information each time until a reasonably accurate picture of the incident is available. But in reality observation of the complete picture is difficult and 'replaying' the incident to get more information is not possible. Therefore, accurate recording of the observed behaviour/situation is essential in order to give meaning to the future care of the individual (*see* French, 1989, pp. 86–92).

In building up a picture of the possible reasons for John's behaviour it is useful to consider the events preceding the behaviour as well as those following it. Consider the following:

1 **The Antecedents** – events taking place immediately before the behaviour occurred.

2 **The Behaviour** – the actual behaviour itself, not supposed or assumed behaviour.

3 **The Consequences** – events/results taking place immediately following the behaviour.

This simple ABC format provides a framework for accurate recording of observations and when used over time can aid understanding of behaviour through effective communication. The accuracy of the written word is paramount to understanding the behaviour of the patient/client. Equally important is the ability of others in the care team to understand and utilise the written word.

Reading and writing together comprise 31 per cent of all communication activities, hence a third of all opportunities for effective communication may be lost through inappropriate or incorrect use of the written word.

The following activity is the final one in this section.

A

Below is a list of instructions. Please read through and complete them before continuing. Make notes if you feel this is relevant. You will need a separate sheet of paper.

1 Write your name on the top left-hand side of the page.
2 Write the date on the top right-hand side of the page.
3 Write your date of birth on the top right-hand side of the paper.
4 What is syntax?
5 Name three types of communication.
6 What does semantic mean?
7 Name two symbolic languages.
8 What is the importance of posture?
9 Follow the instructions carefully.
10 Multiply 0.5 grams x 0.5 grams.
11 Name three components of NVC.
12 Why is communication important?
13 Why should we read instructions with care?
14 The next section is a quick look at the Arts.
15 Now that you have read everything complete only 4, 5, 6, 7, 8, 11 and 12.

For this final activity how many readers followed the instructions and completed only item 15? The activity emphasises the need to read instructions carefully and understand their consequences (under examination conditions, students often fail to read instructions and questions carefully, thus restricting their ability to give effective answers). If you answered the required questions in this activity then the exercise will have provided useful revision of key areas within this chapter.

The Arts

The relevance of the arts to caring professions may, on the face of it, be tenuous; as a symbolic means of communicating, however, the arts provide an alternative to the spoken word. The use of art and music as therapeutic media is well established and you will probably encounter their usage during practical experiences. Acting, painting, music and photography can all be employed to enable patients/clients to communicate, and/or to extend existing means of communicating. The arts allow a person a freedom of expression that is rarely available using the written word, but the rules of structure and semantics must still apply if observers are to understand what the individual is attempting to communicate. Interpretation of patients'/clients' artwork can provide the care team with valuable information regarding their attitude, feelings, progress, abilities and capabilities. The application of such media enhances understanding of the patient/client.

Conclusion

One day in 1873, two goods trains stood at Menheniot station on the Cornwall railway, awaiting instructions from the porter–signalman to proceed. He was in the station telegraph office and the guard of the 'down' train waited on the platform outside. The guard of the 'up' train was not in sight. In due course the porter–signalman received 'line clear' for the down train over the telegraph, and putting his head round the office door shouted 'Right away, Dick.' To his horror, the 'up' train pulled out. It was a heavy train pulled by two engines; the porter–signalman knew it was on a head-on path to a collision with a third goods train already on its way to Menheniot but he was unable to attract the attention of the guard. In the collision, one locomotive was completely destroyed and the other two very seriously damaged. The engine crew were badly injured, one being killed. The unfortunate porter–signalman did not know that the guards of both the goods trains at Menheniot were named Dick.

BIGNALL, V AND FORTUNE, J, 1984

Not all breakdowns in communication have such disastrous consequences, but having completed this chapter you will have realised that without communication the process of caring would be impossible. Nurses and midwives would find that without appropriate and effective methods of communicating, the relationship between themselves and the patient/client would be less than meaningful. Meaningful relationships are a necessity if you are seeking truly to enable the patient/client to restore health or develop to his or her optimum potential.

Similarly, there is a need to consider the nature of communication between members of the multidisciplinary care team. Effective verbal and non-verbal communication skills are essential for team members to work coherently and consistently towards enabling patients/clients to achieve the desired health gains.

Effective communication aids the acquisition of social skills, daily living skills and group skills. Without these the individual encounters difficulty in integrating within society and subsequently may be restricted in the life chances available. In the same way, human development is consequent on the ability to communicate. Without communication we cannot argue, negotiate, agree, compliment, quarrel, compromise, question, answer, warn, advise, teach, learn, consult, solve problems or make decisions.

Alternative communication systems and languages facilitate development for those individuals who would otherwise be hampered by inability to use the spoken or written word. Communication is essential for collaboration, and collaboration is at the core of effective, high quality multiagency provision. Good communication not only ensures the acquisition of desired health gains by the patient/client, but also makes certain that the providing organisation itself is healthy.

References

Adler R B and Towne N (1990) *Looking Out, Looking In – Interpersonal Communication*, 6th edn. Fort Worth: Holt Rinehart and Winston.

Argyle M (1983) *The Psychology of Interpersonal Behaviour*, 4th edn. Harmondsworth: Penguin Books.

Ashworth P M (1980) *Care to Communicate: an investigation into problems of communication between patients and nurses in intensive therapy units*. London: Royal College of Nursing.

Beck R C (1986) *Applying Psychology: Understanding People*, 2nd edn. London: Prentice-Hall International (UK).

Berne E (1968) *Games People Play: The Psychology of Human Relationships*. Harmondsworth: Penguin Books.

Bignall V and Fortune J (1984) *Understanding Systems Failures*. Manchester: Manchester University Press.

Department of Health (1991) *The Patient's Charter – Raising the Standard*. London: HMSO.

Ekman P, Friesen W V and Ellsworth P (1972) *Emotion in the Human Face: Guidelines for Research and an Integration of Findings*. New York: Pergamon.

Finkelhor D (1988) *Nursery Crimes – Sexual Abuse in Day Care*. Newbury Park: Sage Publications.

French P (1989) *Social Skills for Nursing Practice*. London: Croom Helm.

Hall E T (1959) *The Silent Language*. Garden City: Doubleday and Company.

Handy C B (1985) *Understanding Organisations*, 3rd edn. London: Penguin Books.

Hess E H (1975) *The Tell-tale Eye: How your Eyes reveal Hidden Thoughts and Emotions*. New York: Van Nostrand, Reinhold.

Jourard S H (1966) An exploratory study of body accessibility. *British Journal of Social/Clinical Psychology* 5: 221–231.

Kendon A (1972) Some relationships between body motion and speech: an analysis of an example. Reprinted in *Studies in Dyadic Communication*. New York: Pergamon.

Maslow A H (1968) *The Psychology of Being*. New York: Van Nostrand and Reinhold.

Morris D (1977) *Manwatching: A Field Guide to Human Behaviour*. London: Cape.

Morris D (1979) *Gestures, Their Origins and Distribution*. London: Cape.

Pease A (1984) *Body Language – How to Read Others' Thoughts by their Gestures*. London: Sheldon Press.

Sartre J-P, in The Oxford Dictionary of Quotations (1979) 3rd edn. Oxford: Oxford University Press.

Shimoda K, Argyle M and Bitti R (1978) The intercultural recognition of emotional expressions by three national groups – English, Italian and Japanese. *European Journal of Social Psychology* 8: 169–179.

Totman R (1987) *Social Causes of Illness*, 2nd edn. London: Souvenir Press (Educational and Academic).

Self-Evaluation Questions

With various readings stored his empty skull.
Learned without sense, and venerably dull.

CHARLES CHURCHILL (1731–1764)

Self-Evaluation Questions

Chapter 1 – Psychological and Sociological Dimensions

1. Why do people behave as they do?

2. What is psychology?

3. Why is psychology of use to nurses and midwives?

4. How would you outline the major psychological perspectives?

5. What is sociology?

6. What are the major approaches within sociology?

7. What relevance has the study of sociology to nurses and midwives?

8. How would you define a 'society'?

9. What are the common social structures to be found within societies?

10. What are cultures and subcultures?

11. How would you explain cultural variation?

12. Is society constricting or enabling?

13. What are the sources of social order?

14. What is social control?

15. What factors stimulate social change?

16. How would you define the process of socialisation?

17. Do you think childhood influences our later adult interactions and if so how?

18. How might deprivation of social contact be manifested?

19. How might the concepts of socialisation and resocialisation be useful to nurses and midwives?

20. How does conformity differ from compliance?

21. What are the four kinds of norms identified in Chapter 1?

22. Which four variables affect compliance?

23. What are the significant influences on social control?

24. What are the main areas of social conflict in our society?

25. What are the essential features of the sick role?

26. How might adoption of the sick role influence the provision of health care?

27. What factors influence individual deviance?

28. How might you define an attitude and outline their major aspects?

29. How would you describe the components of attitudes?

30. What are the functions of attitudes?

31. What explanations are given for attitude formation?

32. How might you go about changing an individual's attitudes?

33. What are the key components of persuasive communication?

34. How would you explain dissonance theory?

35. How might you assess the appropriateness of seeking attitude change in a given individual?

36. What have you learned from studying this chapter?

Chapter 2 – Divisions in Society

1. Explain briefly why awareness of social divisions is important to care professionals.

2. What is meant by 'class structure'?

3. Adam Smith is often regarded as the founder of capitalism/individualism. What are the central themes of his ideology?

4. How, according to Smith, could social mobility improve an individual's social status?

5. The ideology of Karl Marx provides a clear contrast to that of Adam Smith. What are the main differences?

6. How has Marxist philosophy affected the development of social divisions?

7. Weber's ideology of social divisions focuses on three aspects of a person's life. What are those three aspects?

8. Weber also referred to 'life chances' as opportunities which present themselves to individuals. How do life chances influence a person's social status?

9. How may social status impinge on individual health? Give examples.

10. Why is holistic assessment important?

11. What is meant by 'race'?

12. What are the three main explanations given for racial divisions?

13. Why is 'institutional racism' potentially more damaging than 'personal racism'?

14. What do you now understand by the term 'gender inequalities'?

15. Why is the biological explanation of gender differences, when taken alone, an unsatisfactory one?

16. Outline those social and cultural factors which influence gender differences.

17. How does 'sex typing' occur in society?

18. How does gender differentiation manifest itself within the labour market?

19. Briefly identify why health inequalities occur within modern society.

20. How might the following factors affect an individual's health?

    (i)   Class

    (ii)   Education

    (iii)   Occupation

    (iv)   Income/wealth

21. Poverty and restricted access are widely considered to be interlinked precipitators for poor health. Explain why.

22. What approaches are the government using in an attempt to lessen health inequalities?

23. What personal action can you take to lessen health inequalities and to help patients/clients achieve maximum health gain?

Chapter 3 – Labelling Theory and Stigma

1. Why does labelling occur?

2. What is the relationship between Stockwell's 'good' and 'bad' patient and labelling?

3. What is the importance of perception in the labelling process?

4. Labels can be applied both positively and negatively. How, therefore, do labels enable us to make sense of our world?

5. How can attitudes affect the labelling process?

6. What is 'stereotyping'?

7. Why does stereotyping occur?

8. What is prejudice?

9. Personal experiences can have a profound effect on our prejudices. Explain how and why.

10. 'Intergroup conflict', 'personality factors (the authoritarian personality)' and 'social learning' are three aspects of social interplay. What is the importance of these in the origins of prejudice?

11. What differentiates prejudice from discrimination?

12. Define discrimination.

13. There are three components of attitudes which contribute towards discrimination. What are they?

14. How may discrimination affect individuals?

15. What effects can prejudice and discrimination have upon your nursing practices?

16. How do individuals become stigmatised?

17. Describe what has been identified as the 'vicious circle' of stigma?

18. What affect can stigmatisation have on the individual concerned?

19. What do you understand by the phrase 'professional values'?

20. Why are 'professional values' important to the caring process?

21. What is 'ethical decision-making'?

22. What can you do as nurses and midwives to reduce the negative effects of labelling?

Chapter 4 – Institutions and Institutionalisation

1. Define 'institution'.

2. Define 'institutionalisation'.

3. According to political science, what are the three main institutions in contemporary society?

4. What did Whyte mean by the 'social ethic'?

5. Etzioni's work focuses on social institutions and organisations. What does he say about these?

6. Describe the three identified types of power used by institutions and organisations to ensure compliance to 'required standards of behaviour'.

7. Goffman suggests that individuals are 'multiple-role performers'; what did he mean by 'multiple-role performers'?

8. What do you understand the term 'social identity' to mean?

9. Strauss uses a phrase to describe 'order within organisations'. What is this phrase?

10. Thompson describes the 'life cycle of the institution'. Outline the cycle's five stages.

11. 'Modern institutions foster qualities that are required of people in modern societies.' What are these qualities?

12. What do you understand the term 'total institution' to mean?

13. How do freedom, choice and opportunity influence institutional practices?

14. Describe the characteristics of the institutionalised person.

15. What is meant by 'institutional neurosis'?

16. How can carers avoid implementing and maintaining institutionalising practices?

Chapter 5 – Communication

1. Define 'communication'.

2. Describe the 'linear model' of communication.

3. What is the difference between the 'linear model' and the 'interactive model' of communication?

4. Describe the 'transactional model' of communication.

5. In communication, what is meant by noise?

6. What are 'channels'?

7. What is involved in the process known as 'encoding'.

8. What does French believe to be 'the most important feature of nursing'?

9. Why do human beings communicate?

10. Describe the four needs of communication.

11. Describe how these needs may be affected by ill-health.

12. How are your communication processes affected by others?

13. Why is 'self-concept' important to effective communication?

14. Describe the negative aspects of poor self-concept.

15. Describe the positive effects of good self-concept.

16. What do you understand by the term 'non-verbal communication'?

17. What is 'symbolic representation'?

18. Why is body language significantly related to effective communication?

19. Name Kendon's four functions of gesture.

20. What is the significance of body contact to the caring process?

21. What dilemmas may you face when touching a patient/client?

22. Why is eye contact important to speech?

23. When carers are counselling people, eye contact can provide a wealth of information. Why and how?

24. Why must nurses and midwives be aware of facial expressions?

25. What is 'verbal communication'?

26. What are the rules which govern language?

27. Explain why effective writing and reading is paramount to good nursing care.

Index

housing, discrimination in 79
human relations, principles of 7

identification
  of individuals and groups 60–1
  as influence on attitude 45
identity, social 60–1, 137
ideologies, as areas of social conflict 36
ill-treatment, *see* abuse
illness
  definition 39
  theory of 53
imitation, as influence on attitude 45, 51
inconsistency, attitude/behaviour 43
individualism 64–5, 70
industry, functions of 141
inequalities
  access to health facilities 95–6
  definition 92
  in health 91–3
  see also discrimination
institutional bias 135–6
institutional neurosis 155–6
institutionalisation
  avoidance of institutionalising practices
    160–1
  characteristics induced in individuals by
    155
  and clients' choice 152
  and conformity 154
  definition 144
  effect of 150
  factors resulting in 153, 154
  historical style of 154
  'institutionalised ways' 140
  power of professionals 39
  principles of long-term care 162
  results of 156–7
  techniques of neutralisation 159–60
  in whose interest? 157–9
institutions
  common components 140, 141
  definitions 132–3
  functions of 139–40, 141
  hospitals as 140–2
  institutional racism 83
  interdependence of 140
  as part of social structure 16
  power of 135–6
  power of individuals 148–9
  reorganisation or decay? 143
  roles and 136–8

societal 143–4
  in society 133–4
  stages in life cycle of 142–3
  see also institutionalisation; organisations;
    total institutions
interaction, and social order 20

knowledge, as function of attitudes 44

labels
  and behaviour 104–5
  definition 102
  examples 127
  patients 103, 115–16
  perceptions 104
  reducing negative effects of 124–5
  see also attitudes; discrimination;
    prejudice; stereotyping; stigma
labour
  division of, as part of social structure 16
  and gender 86, 89–91
  sources of 81–2
language
  sign languages 187–8, 202
  symbolic languages 198–9, 202
laws
  as influence on social control 34
  as social norms 29
learning disabilities
  changes in philosophy of services for 158
  discrimination 116
  impact of closure of hospitals 118–19
  stigmatisation 117–18
  and symbolic languages 198–9, 202
learning theories, as influence on attitude
  45–6
life chances 73–4

managers, relationship with 182
Marx, Karl
  and capitalism 67–8
  ideology of 67–8
  occupational element in social grouping 68
  and social divisions 67–8
Marxism
  class system 68
  and cultural variation 17–18
  and health provision 69
  reasons for class divisions 79, 81–2
mobility, social 65, 73
  influence of health on 74–5
  and occupation 74